WIRING DIAGRAMS
for
LIGHT and POWER

by Edwin P. Anderson

revised and updated

by William E. Burke

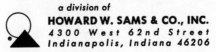

THEODORE AUDEL & CO.
a division of
HOWARD W. SAMS & CO., INC.
4300 West 62nd Street
Indianapolis, Indiana 46206

SECOND EDITION

SECOND PRINTING—1968

WIRING DIAGRAMS FOR LIGHT AND POWER

Library of Congress Catalog Card Number: 63-23291

FOREWORD

The importance of wiring diagrams of electrical machinery and associated relays and instruments is well known to all electrical workers.

This volume has been completely revised and expanded to provide up-to-date reference to the accepted standard wiring diagrams for a wide variety of applications. While it is impossible to cover all possible power system arrangements and operating conditions, attention has been given to the conditions most often encountered in standard practice.

Numerous illustrative, diagrammatic examples are given, especially in the parts dealing with power transformers and synchronizing connection of alternating-current generators, due to the importance of this subject whenever electric energy is generated and transmitted.

Because other symbols and methods of wiring may be possible in electrically equivalent circuits, great care should be observed when connecting electrical apparatus. The diagrams furnished by the manufacturer of equipment to be installed should be followed in each individual case.

E. P. ANDERSON

LIST OF SECTIONS

Note—Each section consists of a related group of diagrams

WIRING
SYMBOLS

WIRING SYMBOLS

INSULATION OR PARTS NOT CARRYING CURRENT	LEADS		CROSS WIRES	CONNECTION WIRING
	POWER OR SERIES	CONTROL OR SHUNT		
------------	▬▬▬	────	┼	┼

TERMINALS		TEST LINK	FLEXIBLE OR PIG TAIL
POWER	CONTROL		
○	○	○──────○	──────○───

THERMAL ELEMENT	LIMIT SWITCHES		VARIAC	RHEOSTAT
○∿∿○	N. C.	N. O.		

METERS			PLUG	RECEPTACLE
NOTE: ON DC INSTRUMENT, + IS ON THE LEFT, BACK VIEW				
AMMETER	VOLTMETER	WATTMETER		
			SHUNT	

WIRING SYMBOLS

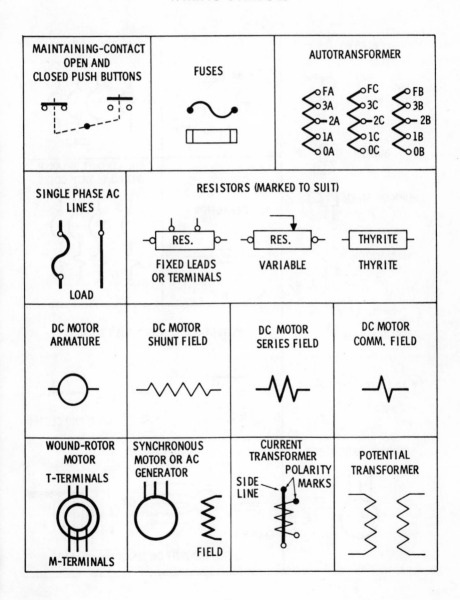

MAINTAINING-CONTACT OPEN AND CLOSED PUSH BUTTONS	FUSES	AUTOTRANSFORMER
		FA FC FB 3A 3C 3B 2A 2C 2B 1A 1C 1B 0A 0C 0B

SINGLE PHASE AC LINES	RESISTORS (MARKED TO SUIT)		
LOAD	RES. FIXED LEADS OR TERMINALS	RES. VARIABLE	THYRITE THYRITE

DC MOTOR ARMATURE	DC MOTOR SHUNT FIELD	DC MOTOR SERIES FIELD	DC MOTOR COMM. FIELD

WOUND-ROTOR MOTOR T-TERMINALS M-TERMINALS	SYNCHRONOUS MOTOR OR AC GENERATOR FIELD	CURRENT TRANSFORMER POLARITY MARKS SIDE LINE	POTENTIAL TRANSFORMER

WIRING SYMBOLS

ALARMS	BATTERY	AIR CIRCUIT BREAKER
BELL		LINES
BUZZER	$+\ \|\ \|\ \|\ -$	SP TP
HORN OR SIREN		LOAD
ANNUNCIATOR	CAPACITOR	AIR CIRCUIT BREAKER WITH O.L. TRIP COILS
		SP TP
		LOAD

SIGNAL LAMPS	MOMENTARY CONTACT PUSH BUTTONS
(W) (R) (G) ETC.	N.O. N.C. OPEN AND CLOSED

SQUIRREL-CAGE MOTOR	CONNECTIONS
	GROUND 5 4 3 2 1 OR 1 2 3 4 5 6 7 8
	CONDUIT OR GROUPING OF LEADS

10

WIRING SYMBOLS

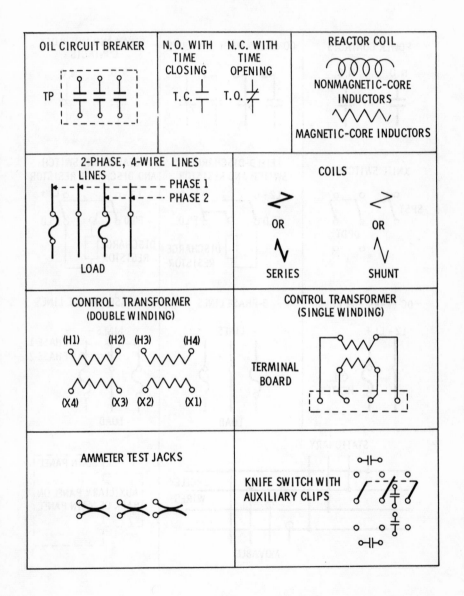

OIL CIRCUIT BREAKER	N.O. WITH TIME CLOSING	N.C. WITH TIME OPENING	REACTOR COIL

TP

T.C.

T.O.

NONMAGNETIC-CORE INDUCTORS

MAGNETIC-CORE INDUCTORS

2-PHASE, 4-WIRE LINES
LINES

PHASE 1
PHASE 2

LOAD

COILS

OR

OR

SERIES

SHUNT

CONTROL TRANSFORMER (DOUBLE WINDING)

(H1) (H2) (H3) (H4)

(X4) (X3) (X2) (X1)

CONTROL TRANSFORMER (SINGLE WINDING)

TERMINAL BOARD

AMMETER TEST JACKS

KNIFE SWITCH WITH AUXILIARY CLIPS

WIRING SYMBOLS

POWER CONTACTS	CONTACTS WITH BLOWOUTS	RELAY AND INTERLOCK CONTACTS
N.O.　　N.C.		N.O.　　N.C.

KNIFE SWITCHES	FIELD-DISCHARGE SWITCH AND RESISTOR	DEAD-FRONT SWITCH AND DISCHARGE RESISTOR
SPST　　DPDT	L2 - o　　o L1 +　F'LD　F'LD　DISCHARGE RESISTOR	L2 - o　　o L1 +　F'LD　F'LD　DISCHARGE RESISTOR

DC (MARK FOR DC)	3-PHASE LINES	2-PHASE, 3-WIRE LINES
L2 - L1 +　O.L. HEATER	LINES　LOAD	LINES　PHASE 1　PHASE 2　LOAD

STATIONARY	
TROLLEY WIRES　MOVABLE	MAIN PANEL　AUXILIARY PANEL ON BACK OF MAIN PANEL

HOUSE WIRING
AND BELLS

VARIOUS LAMP-CONTROL SCHEMES

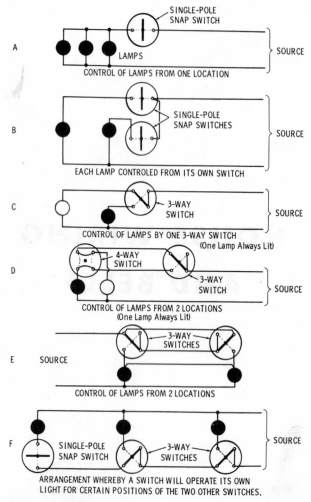

A — SINGLE-POLE SNAP SWITCH — LAMPS — SOURCE
CONTROL OF LAMPS FROM ONE LOCATION

B — SINGLE-POLE SNAP SWITCHES — SOURCE
EACH LAMP CONTROLED FROM ITS OWN SWITCH

C — 3-WAY SWITCH — SOURCE
CONTROL OF LAMPS BY ONE 3-WAY SWITCH
(One Lamp Always Lit)

D — 4-WAY SWITCH — 3-WAY SWITCH — SOURCE
CONTROL OF LAMPS FROM 2 LOCATIONS
(One Lamp Always Lit)

E — SOURCE — 3-WAY SWITCHES
CONTROL OF LAMPS FROM 2 LOCATIONS

F — SINGLE-POLE SNAP SWITCH — 3-WAY SWITCHES — SOURCE
ARRANGEMENT WHEREBY A SWITCH WILL OPERATE ITS OWN
LIGHT FOR CERTAIN POSITIONS OF THE TWO OTHER SWITCHES.

In the lamp-control diagrams represented above, Fig. A illustrates the connection when one single-pole snap switch is used.

Fig. B shows how two lights (or two groups of lights) can be controlled individually from a set of two single-pole switches.

Figs. C to F illustrate a series of special types of lamp control used in test circuits or in any location where particular control schemes are desirable.

14

LAMP CONTROL FROM 2 LOCATIONS

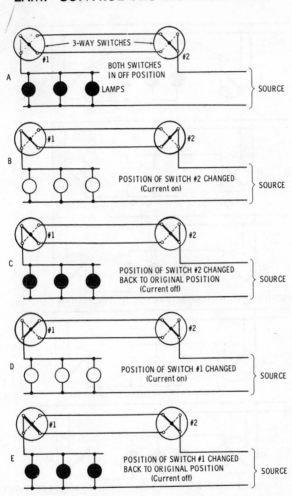

A convenient and often used method for control of a lamp or a group of lamps from two points by means of 3-way switches is shown in the diagrams. The lamps may be extinguished or lighted from either switch regardless of the position of the other. When both switches are in the positions shown in Fig. A, the lamps are extinguished, and can be illuminated by the operation of switch No. 1 or 2. If as shown in diagram, No. 2 switch is operated the lamps will be illuminated, and can now be extinguished from either switch. A typical sequence of operation is shown diagrammatically in Figs. A to E.

LAMP CONTROL FROM 2 LOCATIONS

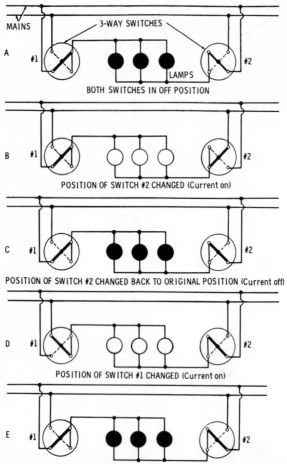

MAINS

3-WAY SWITCHES

A #1 LAMPS #2

BOTH SWITCHES IN OFF POSITION

B #1 #2

POSITION OF SWITCH #2 CHANGED (Current on)

C #1 #2

POSITION OF SWITCH #2 CHANGED BACK TO ORIGINAL POSITION (Current off)

D #1 #2

POSITION OF SWITCH #1 CHANGED (Current on)

E #1 #2

POSITION OF SWITCH #1 CHANGED BACK TO ORIGINAL POSITION (Current off)

This connection provides an economical means of lamp control from two locations. Although not permissible under the National Electric Code, it is shown only as an electrically possible circuit. As in the previous connections shown, both switches are in off position in Fig. A, the lamps are extinguished and can be lit by operating either switch. If switch No. 2, Fig. B is operated to position "S" the lamps will be illuminated and can be extinguished again from any one of the two switches. Figs. A to E inclusive show the lamps lighted or extinguished, depending on position of switch No. 1, relative to the position of switch No. 2.

LAMP CONTROL FROM 2-CIRCUIT
ELECTROLIER SWITCH

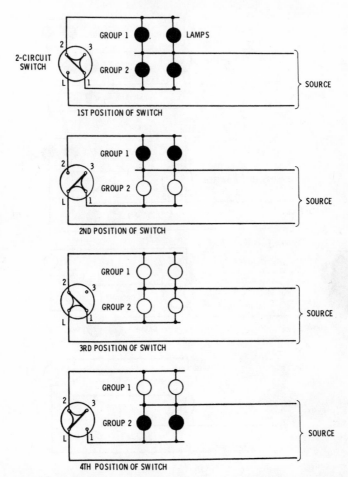

Large fixtures or electroliers are often wired so that lights can be controlled in two or more independent groups. As shown in the diagram the two groups of lamps are extinguished in the first position of the switch. When the switch is moved to the second position, group No. 2 will be illuminated. In the third position the maximum amount of brightness is obtained as both groups of lamps are illuminated; and finally in the fourth position, group No. 1 only is lit. This switch may not be considered as standard, it is only one of several arrangements.

LAMP CONTROL FROM 3-CIRCUIT
ELECTROLIER SWITCH

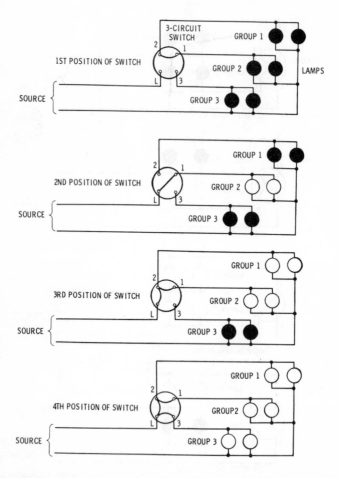

A 3-circuit electrolier switch from which three groups of lamps are controlled is shown above. The sequence of operation is depicted diagrammatically and is principally the same as shown in the previous 2-circuit switch. In the 4th position maximum illumination is obtained, with all lamps lighted. The switch shown is typical only among a great variety of switches manufactured for electrolier or dome-lamp control. The current carrying capacity of the switch as well as potential of the source to be connected should be considered for each individual application.

CONTROL OF LAMPS FROM MORE THAN ONE LOCATION
BY MEANS OF 3-WAY AND 4-WAY SWITCHES

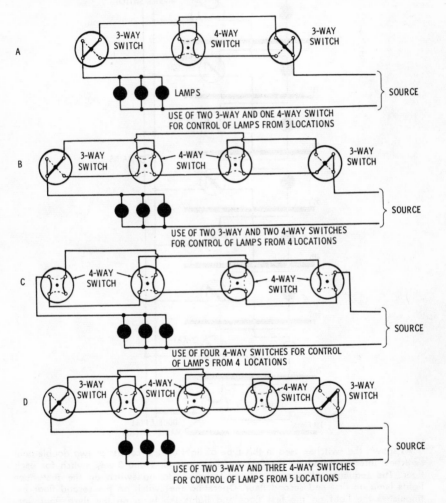

A

3-WAY SWITCH   4-WAY SWITCH   3-WAY SWITCH

LAMPS

SOURCE

USE OF TWO 3-WAY AND ONE 4-WAY SWITCH
FOR CONTROL OF LAMPS FROM 3 LOCATIONS

B

3-WAY SWITCH   4-WAY SWITCH   3-WAY SWITCH

SOURCE

USE OF TWO 3-WAY AND TWO 4-WAY SWITCHES
FOR CONTROL OF LAMPS FROM 4 LOCATIONS

C

4-WAY SWITCH   4-WAY SWITCH

SOURCE

USE OF FOUR 4-WAY SWITCHES FOR CONTROL
OF LAMPS FROM 4 LOCATIONS

D

3-WAY SWITCH   4-WAY SWITCH   4-WAY SWITCH   3-WAY SWITCH

SOURCE

USE OF TWO 3-WAY AND THREE 4-WAY SWITCHES
FOR CONTROL OF LAMPS FROM 5 LOCATIONS

The connection diagrams shown in Figs. A to D, illustrate the conventional methods of lamp control when using 3- and 4-way switches. With reference to Fig. A, it is obvious that for any additional point of control desired a 4-way switch connected the same as the middle switch must be used. See Figs. B to D.

19

STAIRWAY LAMP-CONTROL WIRING

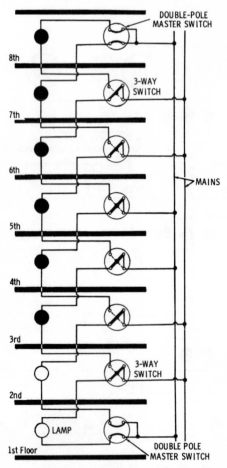

As shown the switches used in this type of light control consist of two double-pole switches, interconnected on the first and last floor, and one 3-way switch for each floor. The sequence of operation is as follows: Closing switch on the first floor lights lamp on first and second floor. Operating the switch on the second floor extinguishes the light on the first floor and lights the lamp on the third floor, etc. This operation is continued until the top floor is reached. In other words the switch on each floor should be operated in passing. It can be readily seen that this light-control arrangement lends itself to operation of lamps irrespective of number of floors encountered.

FLUORESCENT-LAMP CIRCUITS

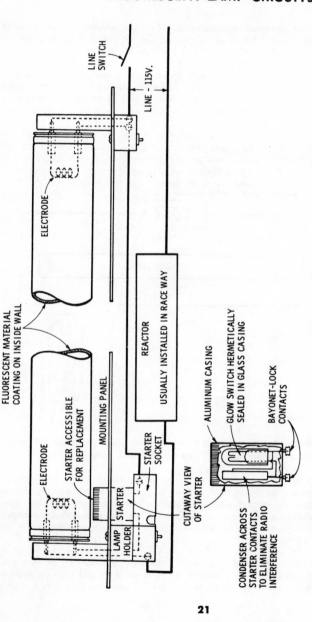

LINE SWITCH

LINE - 115V.

ELECTRODE

FLUORESCENT MATERIAL
COATING ON INSIDE WALL

ELECTRODE

STARTER ACCESSIBLE
FOR REPLACEMENT

MOUNTING PANEL

STARTER
SOCKET

LAMP
HOLDER

STARTER

CUTAWAY VIEW
OF STARTER

REACTOR

USUALLY INSTALLED IN RACE WAY

ALUMINUM CASING

GLOW SWITCH HERMETICALLY
SEALED IN GLASS CASING

BAYONET-LOCK
CONTACTS

CONDENSER ACROSS
STARTER CONTACTS
TO ELIMINATE RADIO
INTERFERENCE

Schematic Diagram of Typical Fluorescent-Lamp Circuit—The necessary auxiliaries for any fluorescent-lamp installation are (1) the ballast, and (2) the starter.

The ballast for operating lamps on 60-cycle AC consists of a small choke coil (reactor) wound on an iron core.

The ballast serves three important functions, namely:

1. It preheats the electrode to make available a large supply of free electrons.
2. It provides a surge of relatively large potential to start the arc between the electrodes.
3. It prevents the arc current increasing beyond the limit set for each size of lamp.

FLUORESCENT-LAMP CIRCUITS

Ballasts—These may be designed for operation of a single lamp or, as is more common, for two lamps mounted in a single fixture. Certain practical advantages are obtained from the choice of an electrical circuit which combines under one cover the equipment for the control of two lamps.

Chief among the advantages are improved power factor, decreased stroboscopic effect and reduced auxiliary losses. Each lamp is operated through a separate choke coil. A capacitor is connected in series with one lamp and its choke coil to give a leading current. The leading and lagging currents will combine with a resulting line power factor of very nearly 100%.

When connecting lamps, ballast and starter into an electric circuit, it is of the utmost importance to observe the manufacturers' diagram usually labeled on the ballast. This diagram should be followed in each instance for proper operation of the lamp or lamps. Also it should be clearly understood that each lamp size must have a ballast designed for its particular wattage, voltage and frequency.

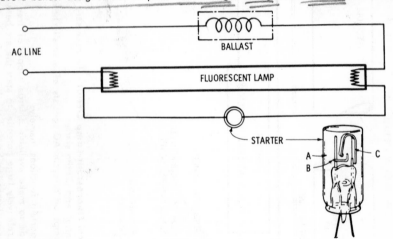

Wiring Diagram of Single Fluorescent Lamp—In the glow-type starter **A,** represents glass bulb filled with inert gas; **B,** fixed electrode; **C,** bimetal strip.

Starters—The starter is designed to act as a time-delay switch which will connect the two filament type electrodes in each end of the lamp in series with the ballast during the short preheating period when the lamp is first turned on and then open the circuit to establish the arc. This preheating causes the emission of electrons from the cathodes and thus makes it possible for the arc to strike without the use of excessively high voltage.

Operation—The switch is enclosed in a small glass bulb and consists of two electrodes, one of which is made from a bimetal strip, in an inert gas such as neon or argon. These electrodes are separated under normal conditions but when closed

FLUORESCENT-LAMP CIRCUITS

form part of a series circuit through the lamp electrodes and the choke coil (ballast).

When voltage is applied, a small current flows as a result of the glow discharge between two electrodes of the switch. Heating of the electrodes results which, by the expansion of the bimetallic element, causes the electrodes to touch. This short circuiting of the switch stops the glow discharge but allows a substantial flow of current to preheat the lamp electrodes. There is enough residual heat in the switch to keep it closed for a short period of time for the electrode preheating. The glow being quenched, the bimetal cools, the switch opens and the resultant high voltage surge starts normal lamp operation. If the lamp arc fails to strike, the cycle is repeated.

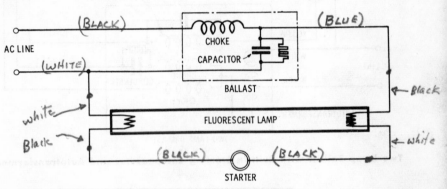

Wiring Diagram of Single Fluorescent Lamp with Capacitor for Improvement of Power Factor—For operation of the 13-, 30-, 40- and 100-watt lamps on 110- to 125-volt circuits, the ballast must include a transformer for stepping up the voltage.

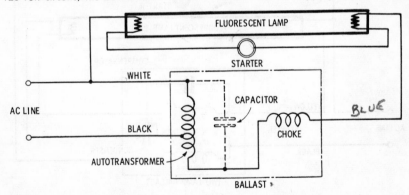

Wiring Diagram of Single Fluorescent Lamp with Power Factor-Corrected Ballast and Autotransformer for Stepping Up the Voltage.

23

FLUORESCENT-LAMP CIRCUITS

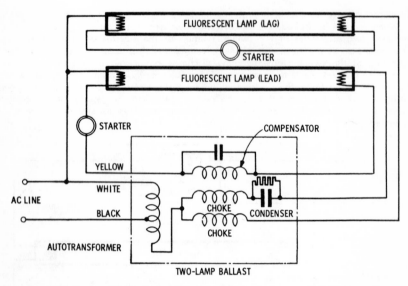

Two-Lamp Ballast with Built-In Starting Compensator and Autotransformer.

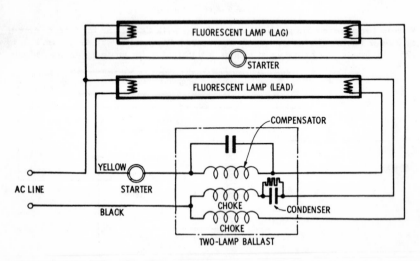

Wiring Diagram of Two-Lamp Ballast with Built-In Starting Compensator.

FLUORESCENT-LAMP CIRCUITS

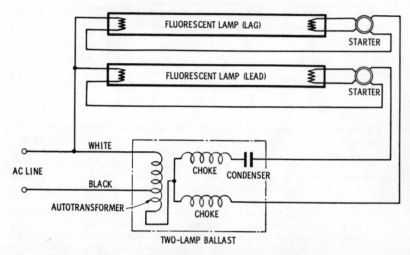

Wiring Diagram of Two-Lamp Ballast with Autotransformer and a Four-Contact Starter Socket for Each Lamp.

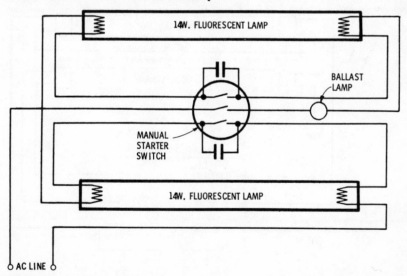

Wiring Diagram for Operating Two 14-Watt Fluorescent Lamps in Series with a Special Incandescent Ballast Lamp.

FLUORESCENT-LAMP CIRCUITS

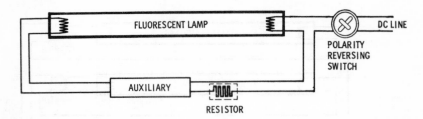

Wiring Diagram of Fluorescent Lamp for Operation on Direct Current—While the fluorescent lamp is basically an alternating-current lamp, it is also used on direct current where alternating current is not available. Due to the lack of voltage peaks when direct current is used, lamp starting is generally more difficult than on alternating current and special starting devices must be used. The thermal and manual switches in addition to a starting inductance are generally employed.

With fluorescent lamps, one end of the tube may become dim after operating a few hours on direct current. This is due to the bombardment of electrons in one direction only. By reversing the direction of current flow at certain intervals (once a day or more frequently if desired) by means of a special reversing switch, this dimming may be eliminated.

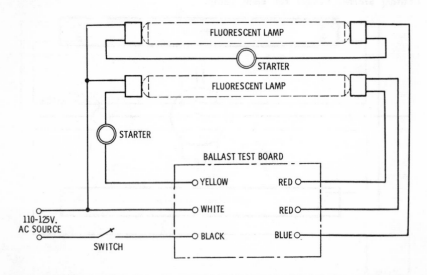

Wiring Arrangement for Ballast Test Board—By means of a circuit of this type, 40-watt, two-lamp ballasts for use on standard voltage may easily be tested. This

FLUORESCENT-LAMP CIRCUITS

is simply a two-lamp circuit with binding posts left at the point where the ballast must be connected in order that quick connections may be made. By providing socket spacing necessary to receive lamps of other sizes, such a test board can be used to check ballasts of any size, provided care is taken to make the connections through the proper binding posts.

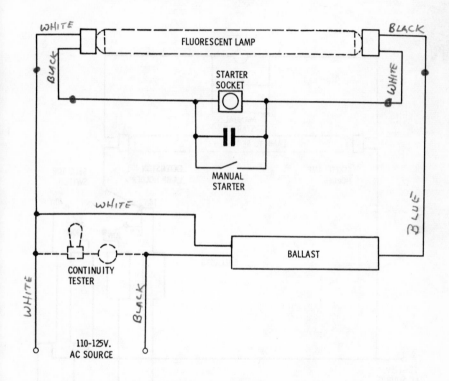

Wiring Diagram Illustrating a Simple Testing Board for Fluorescent Lamps— A test board of this type may be used for checking 40-watt lamps with the lamp holders spaced to receive lamps of the proper size and provided with a starter socket and manual starter switch properly connected to a suitable ballast. A filament-continuity checker can also be included if desired. This consists of a fluorescent-lamp socket in series with an incandescent lamp of 25-watt size or smaller.

A testing board of this type has been found helpful for checking fluorescent lamps and starters to see that they operate satisfactorily.

FLUORESCENT-LAMP CIRCUITS

Lamp boards of this general type may also be made to check lamps of several different sizes by providing the necessary ballasts and the lampholders properly spaced to receive the lamps or one lamp socket mounted stationary and the other provided with pins so that it can be plugged into jacks located at the proper distance for taking lamps of various lengths.

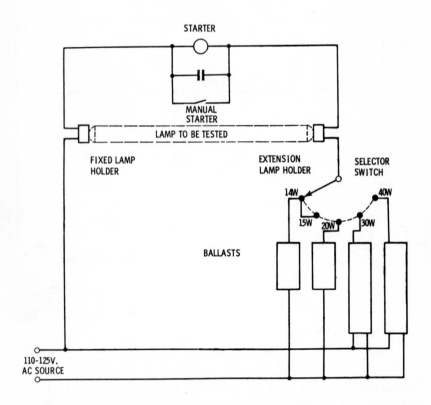

Wiring Diagram of Portable Test Kit for Checking Fluorescent Lamps and Starters—By means of a circuit arrangement of this type various size lamps and starters may be tested directly on the job. All that is required is that the kit be large enough to hold the required ballasts, as connection to one end of the lamp is made by means of a lamp holder on the end of an extension cord. A selector switch must be included for making connections to the proper ballast.

FLUORESCENT-LAMP CIRCUITS

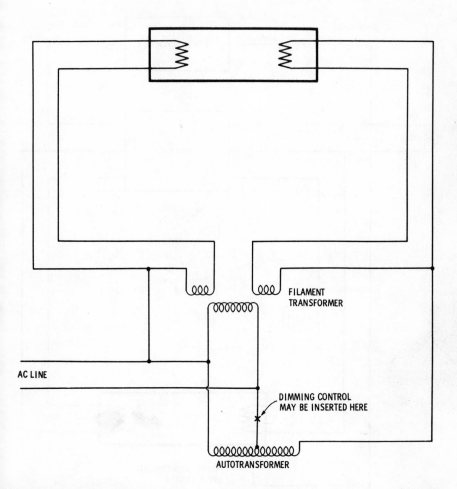

Fluorescent-Lamp Dimming—To dim fluorescent lamps, it is insufficient to merely lower the voltage because the lamp will be extinguished at the zero point of each cycle and the voltage will be insufficient to restrike the arc. The brightness of the lamp will be determined by the current flowing after the arc has been struck. It is necessary to provide an autotransformer to develop enough voltage to strike the arc and a dimming control circuit to control the current after the arc has been established.

FLUORESCENT-LAMP CIRCUITS

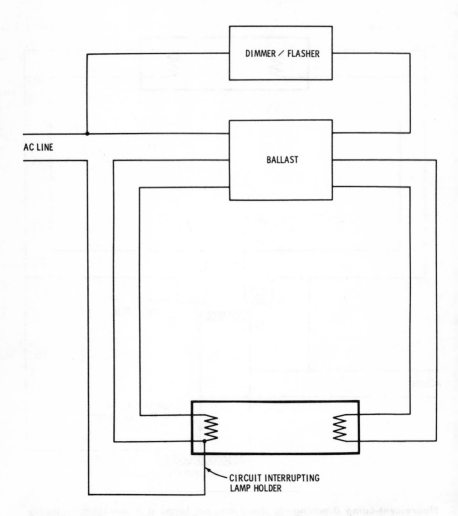

Wiring Diagram for Use of Fluorescent Lamp for Dimming or Flashing—Dimming ballasts and the proper control device make it possible to adjust the light level up or down quickly and easily. Fluorescent lamps used with dimmers offer several advantages over incandescent lamps—higher efficiency, lower operating costs, and better control of color over the dimming range. The flasher device permits the use of fluorescent lamps in display signs and the like.

VARIOUS METHODS OF INSTALLING SERVICE DROPS

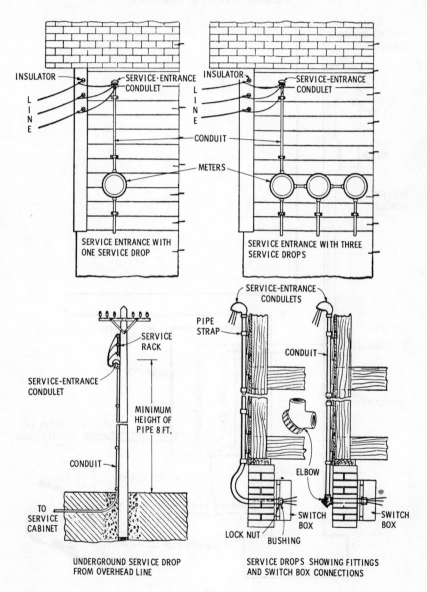

SERVICE ENTRANCE WITH ONE SERVICE DROP

SERVICE ENTRANCE WITH THREE SERVICE DROPS

UNDERGROUND SERVICE DROP FROM OVERHEAD LINE

SERVICE DROPS SHOWING FITTINGS AND SWITCH BOX CONNECTIONS

TYPICAL METHOD OF GROUNDING FOR HOUSE-WIRING SERVICE

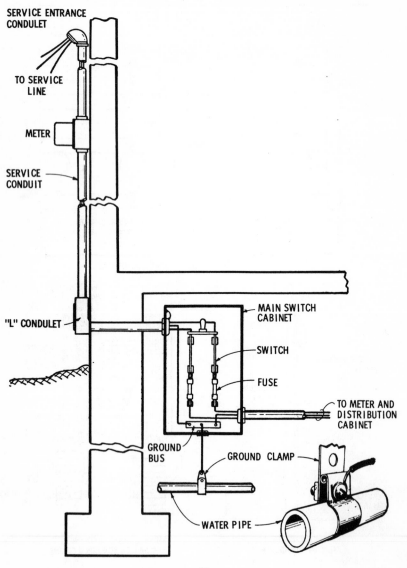

SERVICE ENTRANCE CONDULET

TO SERVICE LINE

METER

SERVICE CONDUIT

"L" CONDULET

MAIN SWITCH CABINET

SWITCH

FUSE

TO METER AND DISTRIBUTION CABINET

GROUND BUS

GROUND CLAMP

WATER PIPE

DIAGRAM OF CONNECTIONS FOR TYPICAL 2-METER SERVICE

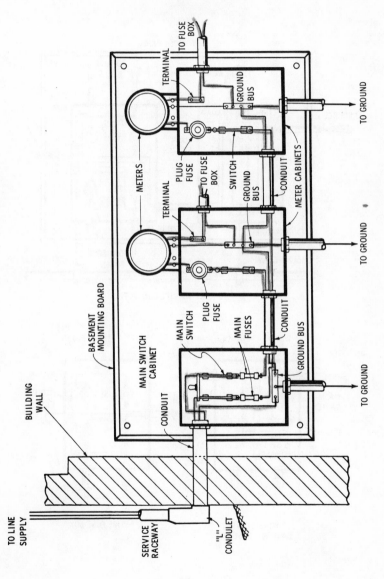

WIRING DIAGRAM OF THREE-WIRE METER
AND SERVICE BOXES

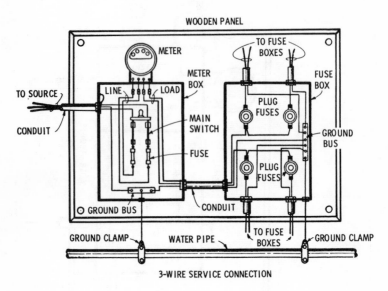

3-WIRE SERVICE CONNECTION

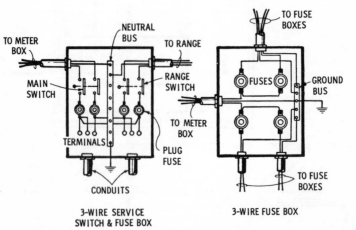

3-WIRE SERVICE
SWITCH & FUSE BOX

3-WIRE FUSE BOX

SERVICE CONNECTIONS FOR A THREE-WIRE SYSTEM

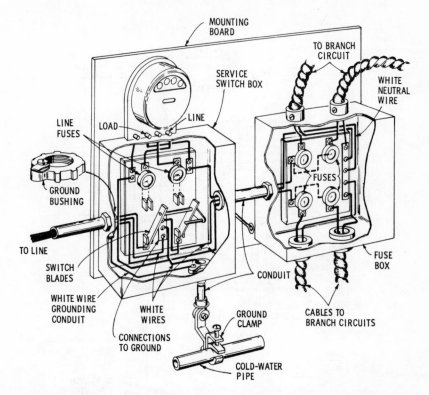

MOUNTING
BOARD

TO BRANCH
CIRCUIT

SERVICE
SWITCH BOX

WHITE
NEUTRAL
WIRE

LINE
FUSES

LOAD

LINE

LINE

GROUND
BUSHING

FUSES

TO LINE

FUSE
BOX

SWITCH
BLADES

CONDUIT

WHITE WIRE
GROUNDING
CONDUIT

WHITE
WIRES

GROUND
CLAMP

CABLES TO
BRANCH CIRCUITS

CONNECTIONS
TO GROUND

COLD-WATER
PIPE

Installation Notes—It is important that all wiring be installed to conform with the requirements of the National Electric Code or any local requirements for safe electrical installation.

The first requirement for any installation is to determine the type and size of load (number of lamps, motors, heating elements, etc. required). When this is done it is a comparatively easy matter to compute the maximum wattage requirements, from which data the current is obtained by Ohm's law.

When the current load for each circuit is known, the size of fuses and wire for the main and branch circuits is determined from wiring tables. In most branch circuits where the maximum load does not exceed 15 amperes, No. 14 wire is used, although in some localities the branch circuit load is limited to 1200 watts (at 110 volts) and no branch circuit may include more than twelve outlets. Generally circuits supplying oil burners, washing machines, refrigerators, electric ranges, and any heating appliance exceeding 1000 watts, are wired on independent circuits, separate from the light circuits. In three-wire systems it is required that the load be balanced or evenly distributed between the ground and the outside wires.

SWITCH BOX AND METHOD OF INSTALLATION

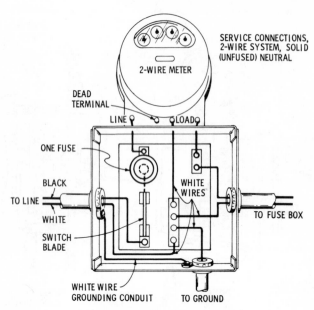

SERVICE CONNECTIONS,
2-WIRE SYSTEM, SOLID
(UNFUSED) NEUTRAL

2-WIRE METER

DEAD
TERMINAL

LINE   LOAD

ONE FUSE

BLACK

TO LINE

WHITE

SWITCH
BLADE

WHITE
WIRES

TO FUSE BOX

WHITE WIRE
GROUNDING CONDUIT

TO GROUND

TYPICAL SERVICE METER BOX
(INTERIOR VIEW)

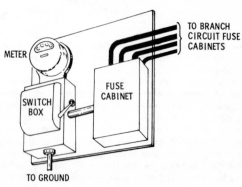

TO BRANCH
CIRCUIT FUSE
CABINETS

METER

FUSE
CABINET

SWITCH
BOX

TO GROUND

TYPICAL BASEMENT INSTALLATION
(EXTERIOR VIEW)

WIRING DIAGRAM OF VARIOUS BRANCH-CIRCUIT FUSE BOXES

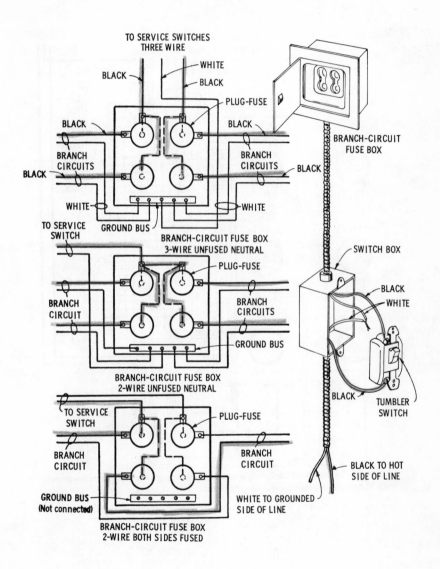

TO SERVICE SWITCHES
THREE WIRE

WHITE

BLACK

BLACK

PLUG-FUSE

BLACK

BLACK

BRANCH
CIRCUITS

BRANCH
CIRCUITS

BLACK

BRANCH-CIRCUIT
FUSE BOX

BLACK

BLACK

WHITE

WHITE

TO SERVICE
SWITCH

GROUND BUS

BRANCH-CIRCUIT FUSE BOX
3-WIRE UNFUSED NEUTRAL

PLUG-FUSE

SWITCH BOX

BRANCH
CIRCUIT

BRANCH
CIRCUITS

BLACK

WHITE

GROUND BUS

BRANCH-CIRCUIT FUSE BOX
2-WIRE UNFUSED NEUTRAL

TO SERVICE
SWITCH

PLUG-FUSE

BLACK

TUMBLER
SWITCH

BRANCH
CIRCUIT

BRANCH
CIRCUIT

GROUND BUS
(Not connected)

BLACK TO HOT
SIDE OF LINE

WHITE TO GROUNDED
SIDE OF LINE

BRANCH-CIRCUIT FUSE BOX
2-WIRE BOTH SIDES FUSED

37

CONNECTION DIAGRAM OF A COMBINATION METER AND CONTROL PANEL BOARD FOR APARTMENT HOTEL

NOTE: This panel arrangement is typical only. Any other arrangement may be used to suit individual needs. The distribution method selected shall, however, in all details comply with the NATIONAL ELECTRIC CODE and any local specification.

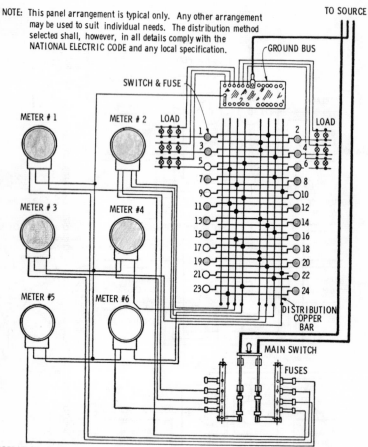

OPERATION: For the sake of clarity only six meters are shown, one of which is a three-wire meter. Meter #1 measures energy consumption in circuits #2, 3, 13, 18 and 19.

"	2	"	"	"	"	"	4, 6, 7, 11, 15, 22 and 24.
"	3	"	"	"	"	"	1, 14 and 20
"	4	"	"	"	"	"	8, 12 and 16
"	5	"	"	"	"	"	9 and 21
"	6	"	"	"	"	"	5, 10, 17 and 23

CONNECTION OF WATTHOUR METER
(FRONT VIEWS)

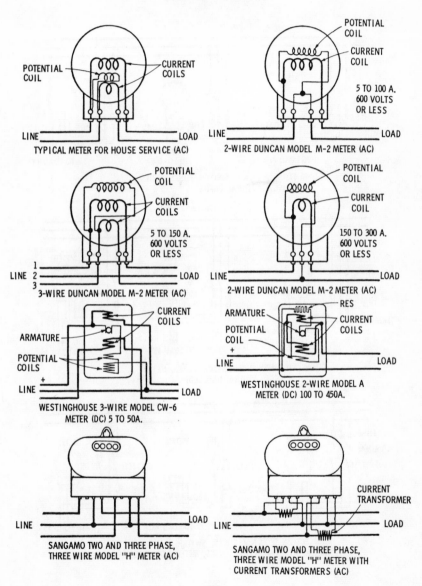

POTENTIAL COIL

CURRENT COILS

LINE

LOAD

TYPICAL METER FOR HOUSE SERVICE (AC)

POTENTIAL COIL

CURRENT COIL

5 TO 100 A.
600 VOLTS
OR LESS

LINE

LOAD

2-WIRE DUNCAN MODEL M-2 METER (AC)

POTENTIAL COIL

CURRENT COILS

5 TO 150 A.
600 VOLTS
OR LESS

LINE 1 2 3

LOAD

3-WIRE DUNCAN MODEL M-2 METER (AC)

POTENTIAL COIL

CURRENT COIL

150 TO 300 A.
600 VOLTS
OR LESS

LINE

LOAD

2-WIRE DUNCAN MODEL M-2 METER (AC)

CURRENT COILS

ARMATURE

POTENTIAL COILS

LINE

LOAD

WESTINGHOUSE 3-WIRE MODEL CW-6
METER (DC) 5 TO 50A.

RES

ARMATURE

CURRENT COILS

POTENTIAL COIL

LINE

LOAD

WESTINGHOUSE 2-WIRE MODEL A
METER (DC) 100 TO 450A.

LINE

LOAD

SANGAMO TWO AND THREE PHASE,
THREE WIRE MODEL "H" METER (AC)

CURRENT TRANSFORMER

LINE

LOAD

SANGAMO TWO AND THREE PHASE,
THREE WIRE MODEL "H" METER WITH
CURRENT TRANSFORMERS (AC)

EXTERNAL CONNECTION DIAGRAMS OF WATTHOUR METERS

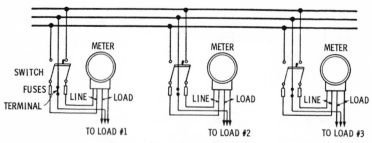

CONNECTION SEQUENCE: SWITCH, FUSES, METER
(NOTE: NEUTRAL UNFUSED)

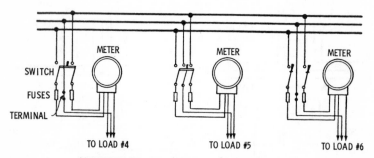

CONNECTION SEQUENCE: SWITCH, FUSES, METER
(NOTE: NEUTRAL UNFUSED)

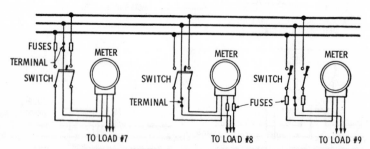

CONNECTION SEQUENCE: FUSES, SWITCH, METER—SWITCH,
METER, FUSES— SWITCH, FUSES, METER (NOTE: NEUTRAL UNFUSED)

INTERNAL CONNECTION OF BELLS

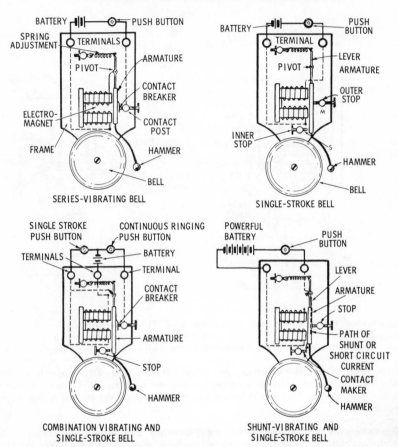

SERIES-VIBRATING BELL

SINGLE-STROKE BELL

COMBINATION VIBRATING AND
SINGLE-STROKE BELL

SHUNT-VIBRATING AND
SINGLE-STROKE BELL

Operation of Series-Vibrating Bell—When the push button is operated, the current energizes the magnet and attracts the armature, causing the hammer to strike the bell, but before it reaches the end of the stroke the contact breaker breaks the circuit, and the hammer, influenced by the tension of the armature spring rapidly moves back to its initial position, thus completing the cycle.

Operation of Single-Stroke Bell—When the push button is operated the current energizes the magnet and attracts the armature, causing the hammer to strike the bell. The armature remains in the attracted position so long as the current flows through the magnet. When connection with the battery is broken, the hammer spring pulls the armature back against **M.** A stop **S,** averts the motion of the armature, momentum springing the lever and causing the hammer to strike the bell.

INTERNAL CONNECTION OF BELLS

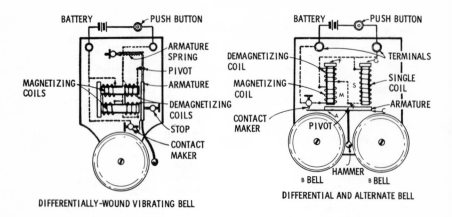

DIFFERENTIALLY-WOUND VIBRATING BELL

DIFFERENTIAL AND ALTERNATE BELL

Operation of Combination Vibrating and Single-Stroke Bell—This bell is essentially a vibrating bell with the addition of a third terminal and a stop to prevent continued contact of the hammer with the bell when working single stroke.

Operation of Shunt-Vibrating and Single-Stroke Bell—This is simply an ordinary shunt bell with a switch arranged so that the short circuit through the contact maker, armature, and lever may be cut out, thus restricting the current to the magnet winding.

Operation of Differentially-Wound Vibrating Bell—When the battery circuit is closed, current flows through the magnetizing winding and energizes the magnets which in turn attract the armature. The contact maker closes the circuit through the demagnetizing coils, which demagnetize the magnets. The armature spring pulls the armature back against the stop, while the contact maker breaks the circuit through the demagnetizing coils.

Operation of Differential and Alternate Bell—When the battery circuit is closed by means of the push button, current flows through the magnetizing winding **M** and energizes **F**, which attracts end **A** of the armature. The contact maker closes circuit through magnetizing coil, and the single coil **S**, of magnet **G**. Then the demagnetizing coil demagnetizes **F**, and as a result, magnet **G** attracts end **C** of the armature. The contact maker breaks the circuit through demagnetizing coil **D**, and single coil **S** of magnet **G**, completing the operation cycle.

42

VARIOUS BELL CIRCUITS

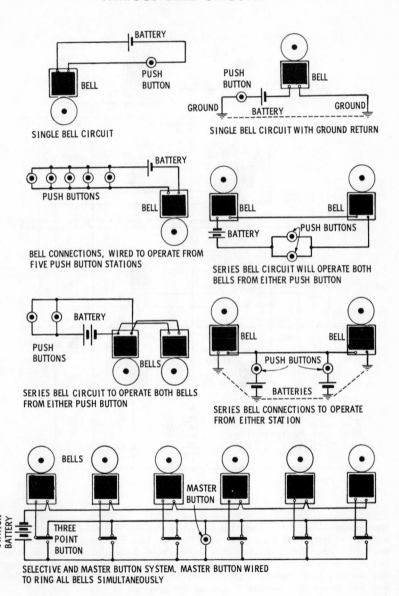

BATTERY

PUSH BUTTON

BELL

SINGLE BELL CIRCUIT

BELL

PUSH BUTTON

GROUND   GROUND
BATTERY

SINGLE BELL CIRCUIT WITH GROUND RETURN

BATTERY

PUSH BUTTONS

BELL

BELL CONNECTIONS, WIRED TO OPERATE FROM
FIVE PUSH BUTTON STATIONS

BELL   BELL

BATTERY   PUSH BUTTONS

SERIES BELL CIRCUIT WILL OPERATE BOTH
BELLS FROM EITHER PUSH BUTTON

BATTERY

PUSH BUTTONS

BELLS

SERIES BELL CIRCUIT TO OPERATE BOTH BELLS
FROM EITHER PUSH BUTTON

BELL   BELL

PUSH BUTTONS

BATTERIES

SERIES BELL CONNECTIONS TO OPERATE
FROM EITHER STATION

BELLS

MASTER
BUTTON

STATION BATTERY

THREE
POINT
BUTTON

SELECTIVE AND MASTER BUTTON SYSTEM. MASTER BUTTON WIRED
TO RING ALL BELLS SIMULTANEOUSLY

43

WIRING DIAGRAM FOR BELLS IN APARTMENT BUILDING

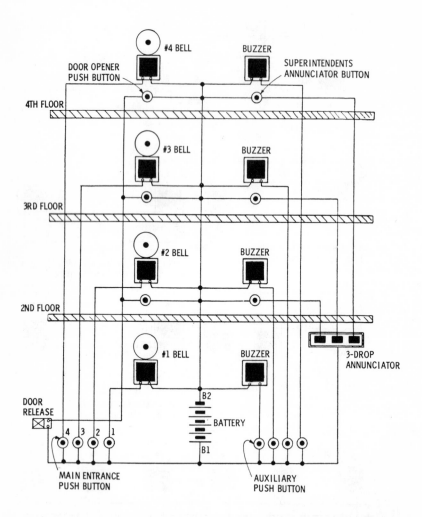

Operation—When for example, push button to apartment on 4th floor is operated, a circuit is completed from battery B_1 through bell #4 and to battery B_2 causing the bell to ring. Similarly when door opener push button on 4th floor is pressed, a circuit is formed from battery B_2 energizing the release coil, which opens the door. The auxiliary push buttons from the service entrance function in a similar manner, notifying tenant by means of buzzer of the presence of service man.

ELECTRIC-METER READING

How to Read an Electric Meter—At certain intervals of time—usually once a month—a consumer of electricity is billed for the amount of electrical energy in kilowatt-hours registered by the meter located on the premises. In order to facilitate the reading of meters, the front of the meter is usually equipped with four equally divided dials as shown in the figures below. It should be observed that each division on the **first right-hand** dial represents one kilowatt-hour or unit. (One kilowatt-hour equals 1,000 watt-hours.) Beginning with this dial read each dial to the left in succession, placing the figures in the same order as read; always make sure to take those figures which the dial finger actually has passed. If uncertain if the dial finger has actually passed a certain figure or not, note whether the next dial has passed its zero (0), remembering that no dial finger has completed a division until the dial finger next to the right has made a complete revolution.

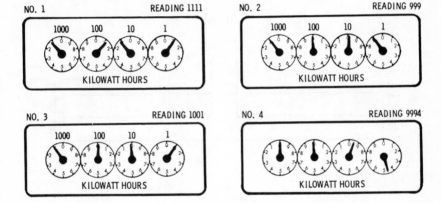

The relation between the speeds of all dial fingers is ten to one, i.e. one complete revolution of one dial hand indicates one division on the next dial to the left. If the above precautions are observed, it is a simple matter to read any meter. For example, the meter shown in example No. 1, indicates one on the dial at the extreme right, the two next following indicate one each and finally the last dial also indicates one, making the total register reading 1111 or a registration of 1111 kilowatt hours.

The reading example represented by meter No. 2 in a similar manner indicates 9 on the dial at the extreme right; the second dial finger rests on 0, but since the first rests only on 9 and has not as yet completed its revolution, it follows that the second dial finger also indicates 9. This 9 placed before 9 already obtained gives 99. The same is true about the third dial. The second dial finger at 9 has not as yet completed its revolution so the third has not completed its division; hence another 9 is obtained making 999. The number of kilowatt-hours registered on meters Nos. 3 and 4 will similarly be obtained, being 1001 and 9994 respectively.

REMOTE-CONTROL WIRING

The heart of the remote-control system is a single-pole, single-throw, double-coil relay. The coils of this relay are operated from a 24-volt transformer and remote switches. Essentially, low-voltage residential control switching provides for turning lights and appliances **on** and **off** remotely either within a house, its surrounding grounds, or other buildings on the property.

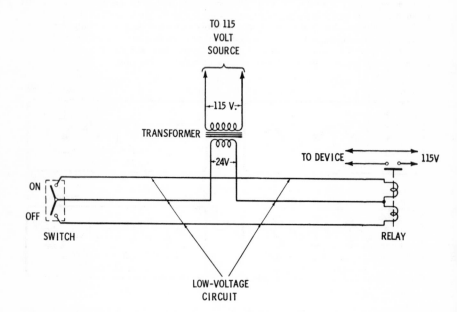

Schematic Diagram of Remote-Control Wiring Circuit Showing One Relay Controlled from One Switch—The relay contacts are operated by momentarily energizing either the opening or the closing coils. The contacts remain latched in either the opening or closed position with no further application of control power.

The relay is mounted by inserting the metal barrel through a one-half inch knockout in a standard outlet box or other metal enclosure. Spring actuated dogs hold the relay in position when installed.

When installed the necessary physical separation of the power circuit and the control circuits as required by the National Electrical Code is automatically established with the power circuits confined in the metal enclosure of the raceway, and the control circuit isolated by being on the outside.

REMOTE-CONTROL WIRING

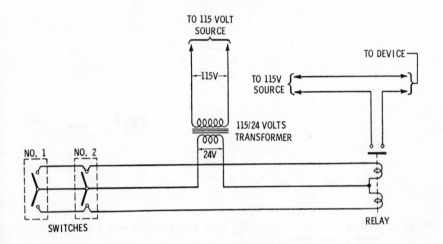

Schematic Diagram of Remote-Control Wiring Circuit Showing One Relay Controlled from Either One of Two Push Button Stations.

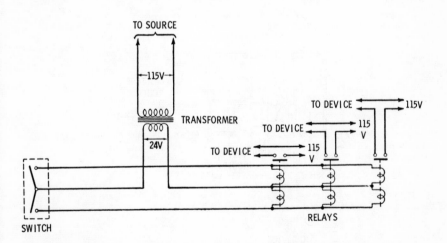

Schematic Diagram Showing a Number of Relays Controlled from a Single Push Button Station.

REMOTE-CONTROL WIRING

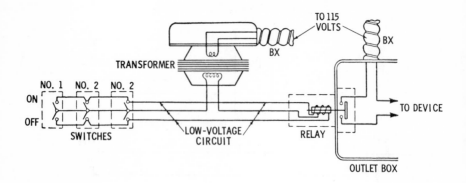

Pictorial Wiring Diagram Illustrating One Relay Controlled from Any One of Three Push Button Stations.

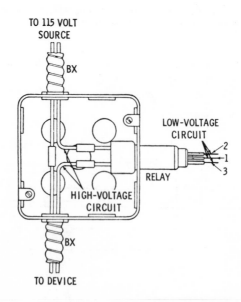

Remote-Control Relay Mounted in Outlet Box.

REMOTE-CONTROL WIRING

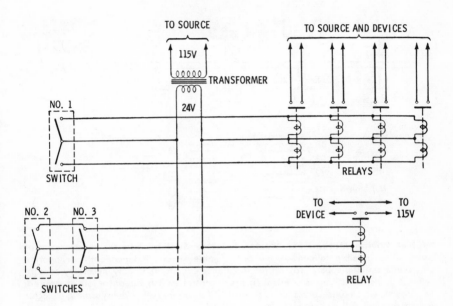

Method of Transformer Connection for Two or More Branch Circuits.

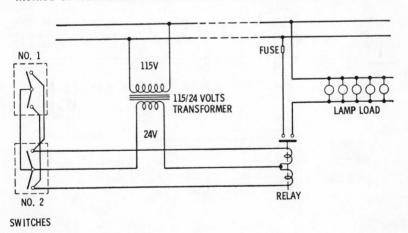

Group of Lamps Controlled from Either One of Two Push Button Stations.

REMOTE-CONTROL WIRING

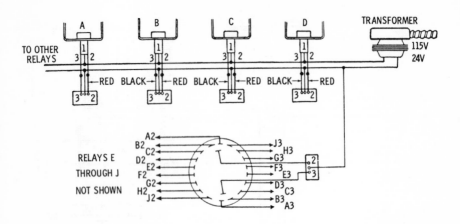

Typical Wiring Method for Master Selector Switch—With the master selector switch it is possible to control any one of nine circuits independently or operate all circuits simultaneously. To control individual circuits, it is only necessary to turn selector switch to circuit desired, then press control switch for on or off as desired. To control all circuits, press control switch for on or off, while turning selector switch through full sweep of all nine positions.

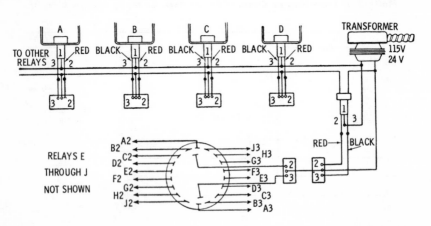

Remote-Control Wiring Hook-Up Showing Connections to Master Selector Switch with Lockout Circuit.

METERS
AND
CONNECTIONS

AMMETER CONNECTIONS

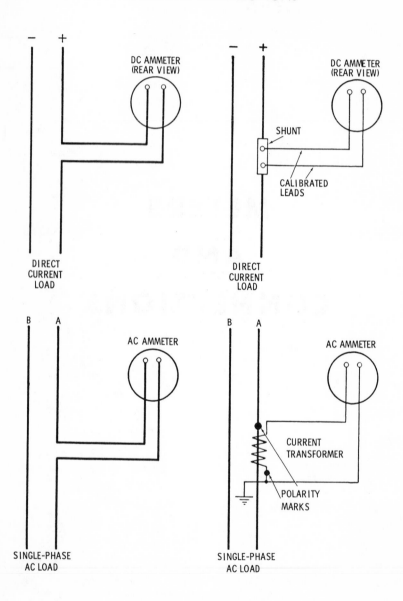

VOLTMETER AND AMMETER CONNECTIONS

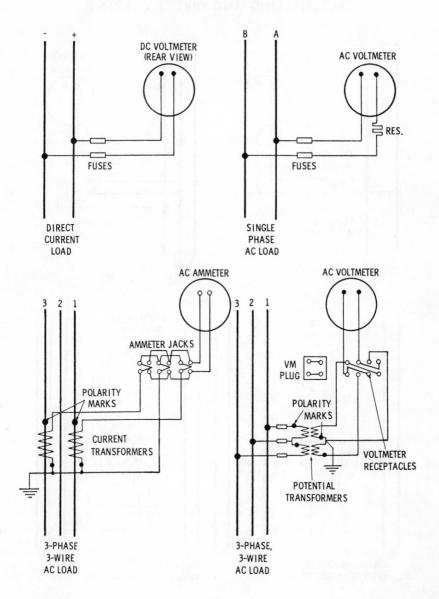

VOLTMETER CONNECTIONS FOR
ALTERNATING AND DIRECT CURRENT

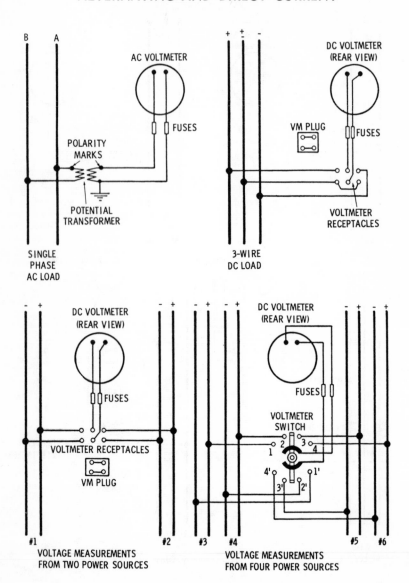

METER CONNECTIONS

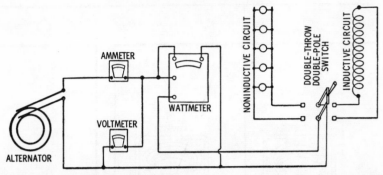

Diagram Illustrating Power-Factor Test on Noninductive and Inductive Circuits—The instruments are connected as shown and by means of the double-throw switch can be put on either the noninductive or inductive circuit. First turn switch to left so that current passes through the lamps; for illustration, the following readings are assumed: ammeter 10, voltmeter 110, and wattmeter 1,100. The power factor then is wattmeter reading ÷ volts × amperes = 1,100 actual watts ÷ 1,100 apparent watts = 1, that is, on noninductive circuits, the power factor is unity. Now the switch is thrown to the right connecting instruments with the inductive circuit, then for illustration, the following readings may be assumed: ammeter 8, voltmeter 110, and wattmeter 684. Now, as before, power factor = wattmeter reading ÷ volts × amperes = 684 ÷ (8 × 110) = 684 ÷ 880 = .78.

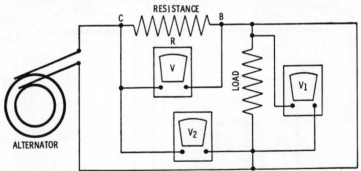

Ayrton and Sumpner Method of Alternating-Current Power Measurement—Three voltmeters are required, and accordingly the method is sometimes called the three-voltmeter method. It is a good method where the voltage can be regulated to suit the load. In the figure, let the noninductive resistance R, be placed in series with the load AB. Measure the following voltages: V, across the terminals of R, V_1, across the load AB, and V_2, across both, that is, from A to C. Then, true watts = $(V_2^2 - V_1^2 - V^2) \div 2R$. The best conditions are when $V = V_1$, and, if $R = \frac{1}{2}$ ohm, then $W = V_2^2 - V_1^2 - V^2$.

METER CONNECTIONS

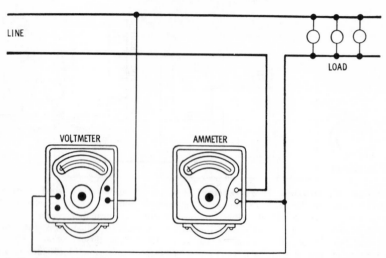

Typical Connection Diagram of Voltmeter and Ammeter in a Single-Phase Circuit—When the instruments are connected as shown, the voltmeter measures load voltage, not line voltage. The ammeter measures load current plus voltmeter current.

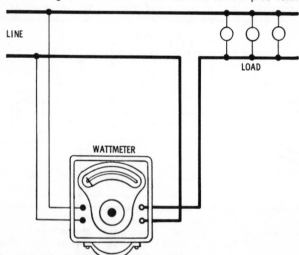

Typical Wattmeter Connection in a Single-Phase Circuit—When connected as shown, the instrument is measuring power load plus losses in its own current coil circuit. If the instrument reads backwards, reverse the current leads.

METER CONNECTIONS

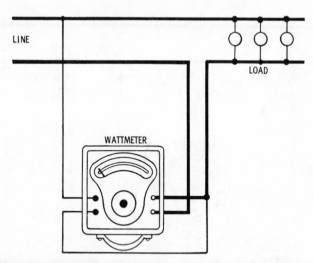

Typical Wattmeter Connection in a Single-Phase Circuit—When connected as shown, the instrument is measuring power load plus losses in its own potential circuit. If the instrument reads backwards, reverse the current leads.

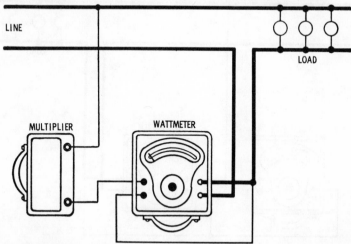

Typical Wattmeter Connection in a Single-Phase Circuit, When Used with Potential Multiplier—When connected as shown the instrument is measuring power load plus losses in its own potential and multiplier circuit.

METER CONNECTIONS

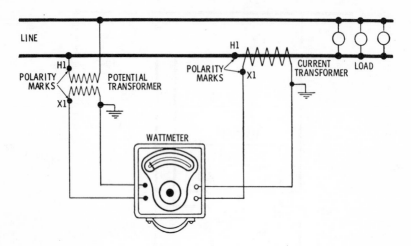

Typical Wattmeter Connections in a Single-Phase Circuit, When Used with Potential and Current Transformer.

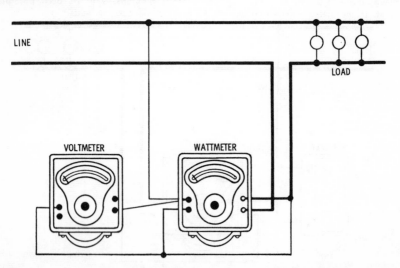

Typical Wattmeter and Voltmeter Connections in a Single-phase Circuit— When connected as shown the wattmeter measures power load plus losses in the voltmeter and wattmeter potential circuits.

METER CONNECTIONS

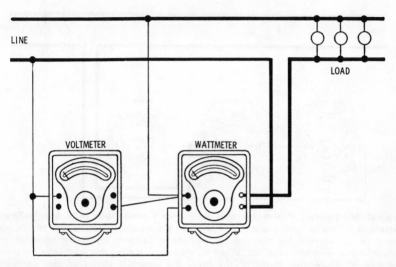

Typical Voltmeter and Wattmeter Connections in a Single-Phase Circuit—
When connected as shown, the wattmeter measures power load plus losses in its
own current-coil circuit.

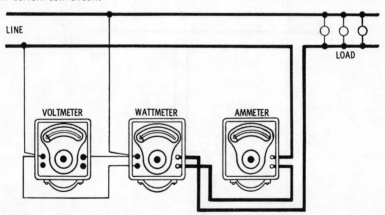

**Typical Wattmeter, Voltmeter and Ammeter Connections in a Single-Phase
Circuit**—In a meter combination of this type the power factor of the circuit may
easily be determined by dividing the wattmeter reading by the product of the
voltmeter and ammeter readings. When connected as shown, the wattmeter measures
power load plus losses in the ammeter and wattmeter current-coil circuit.

METER CONNECTIONS

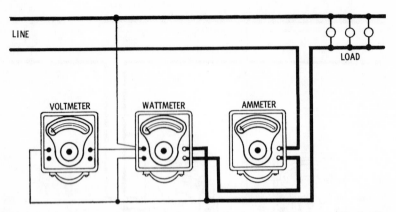

Typical Wattmeter, Voltmeter and Ammeter Connections in a Single-Phase Circuit—In a meter combination of this type, the power factor of the circuit may easily be determined by dividing the wattmeter reading by the product of the voltmeter and ammeter readings. When connected as shown the wattmeter measures the sum of the power losses of the load, the potential circuit of the wattmeter and the voltmeter.

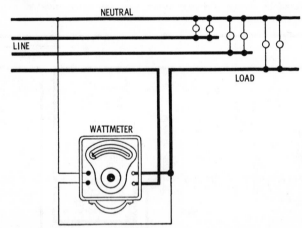

Typical Connection Diagram of a Single Wattmeter in a Balanced Three-Phase, Four-Wire Circuit—While only the wattmeter connections are shown, the voltmeter and ammeter may be connected as illustrated previously. When connected as shown, the power of the system is three times the indication of the single wattmeter. The wattmeter indicates its own potential losses plus the power in one phase of the load.

METER CONNECTIONS

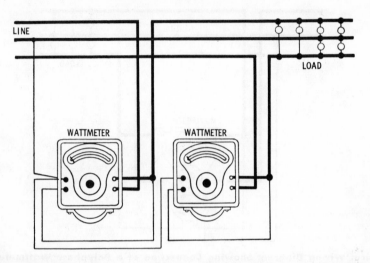

Typical Connection Diagram of Voltmeter and Ammeter in a Single-Phase Circuit—When the instruments are connected as shown, the voltmeter measures line voltage, not load voltage. The ammeter measures load current only.

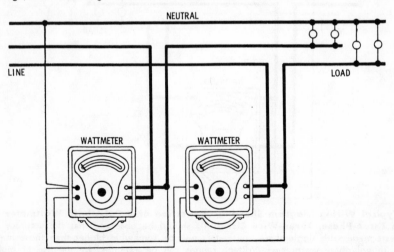

Typical Wiring Diagram Showing Two Wattmeters Connected for Two-Phase, Three-Wire Balanced or Unbalanced Load.

METER CONNECTIONS

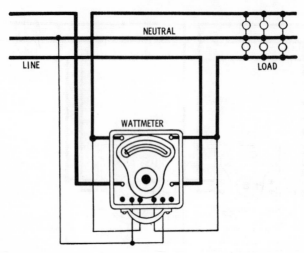

Typical Wiring Diagram Showing Connection of a Polyphase Wattmeter in a Two-Phase, Three-Wire Circuit, Balanced or Unbalanced Voltage or Load.

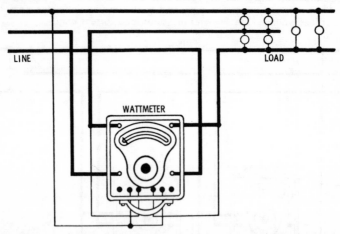

Typical Wiring Diagram Showing Connection of a Polyphase Wattmeter in a Three-Phase, Three-Wire Circuit—It should be observed that the accuracy of tests made with single-phase wattmeters will be somewhat higher than those made with polyphase wattmeters. Voltage ranges can be extended by the use of multipliers or transformers. To obtain high accuracy the instruments should be used at 40% of rated current or above.

METER CONNECTIONS

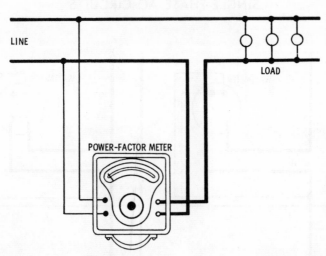

Typical Power-Factor-Meter Connection When Used on a Single-Phase Circuit—Single-phase, power-factor meters should be used only at the calibrated frequency.

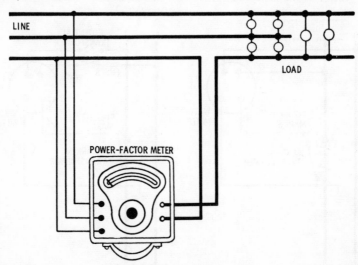

Typical Power-Factor-Meter Connection When Used on a Three-Phase, Three-Wire Circuit.

WATTMETER CONNECTIONS FOR
SINGLE-PHASE AC CIRCUITS

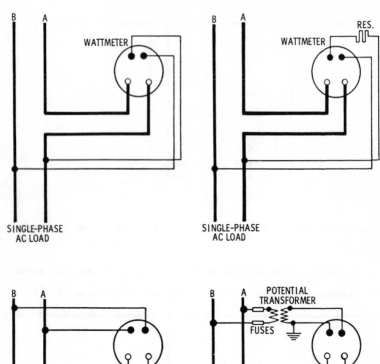

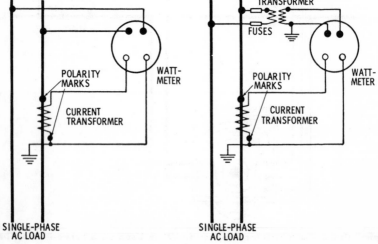

WATTMETER AND VOLTMETER CONNECTIONS IN SINGLE-PHASE AC CIRCUITS

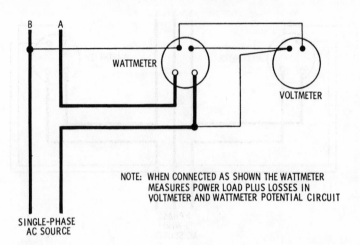

WATTMETER

VOLTMETER

B A

SINGLE-PHASE
AC SOURCE

NOTE: WHEN CONNECTED AS SHOWN THE WATTMETER
MEASURES POWER LOAD PLUS LOSSES IN
VOLTMETER AND WATTMETER POTENTIAL CIRCUIT

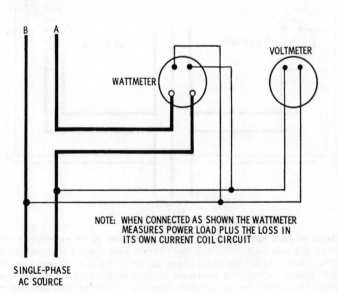

WATTMETER

VOLTMETER

B A

SINGLE-PHASE
AC SOURCE

NOTE: WHEN CONNECTED AS SHOWN THE WATTMETER
MEASURES POWER LOAD PLUS THE LOSS IN
ITS OWN CURRENT COIL CIRCUIT

TWO WATTMETER CONNECTIONS FOR POWER MEASUREMENT

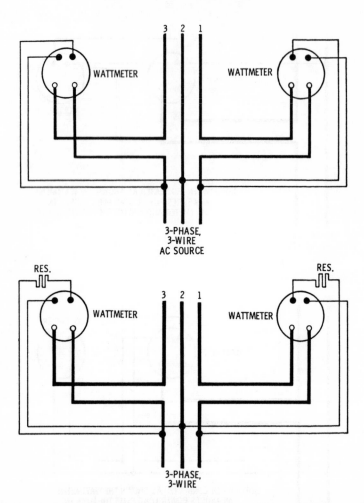

Connections of Two Wattmeters for Measurement of Power—When connected as illustrated, the two wattmeters will not indicate alike even if the load is balanced. Above 50% power factor, the three-phase power is the sum of the two readings. Below 50% power factor, it is necessary to reverse the reading of one wattmeter (by reversing its current leads) and then take the difference between the readings of the two meters.

WATTMETER CONNECTIONS,
SINGLE-PHASE AND POLYPHASE

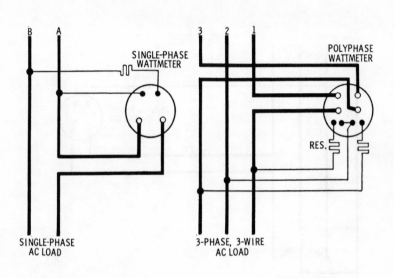

B A

SINGLE-PHASE
WATTMETER

SINGLE-PHASE
AC LOAD

3 2 1

POLYPHASE
WATTMETER

RES.

3-PHASE, 3-WIRE
AC LOAD

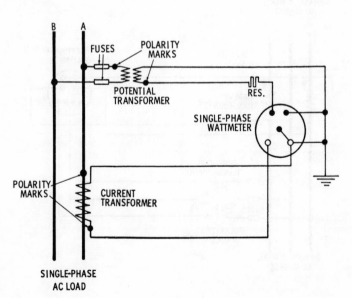

B A

FUSES   POLARITY
MARKS

POTENTIAL
TRANSFORMER

RES.

SINGLE-PHASE
WATTMETER

POLARITY
MARKS

CURRENT
TRANSFORMER

SINGLE-PHASE
AC LOAD

WATTMETER CONNECTIONS, SINGLE-PHASE AND POLYPHASE

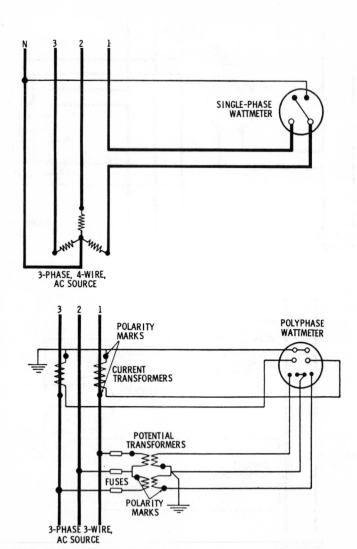

N   3   2   1

SINGLE-PHASE
WATTMETER

3-PHASE, 4-WIRE,
AC SOURCE

3   2   1

POLARITY
MARKS

POLYPHASE
WATTMETER

CURRENT
TRANSFORMERS

POTENTIAL
TRANSFORMERS

FUSES

POLARITY
MARKS

3-PHASE 3-WIRE,
AC SOURCE

WATTHOUR-METER TEST

A watthour meter is used for measurement of electric energy. Principally it consists of an electric motor with associated windings so arranged that the mechanical torque produced indicates the electrical power.

One winding of the meter is usually connected in series with the load and the other across the circuit. The torque of such a motor will be proportional to the power and the total revolutions of the motor will be a measure of energy consumed by the load.

In addition a watthour meter is equipped with a register which records the revolutions of the meter shaft and a magnetic brake whose function it is to retard the revolutions of the motor.

Due to the inability of most meters to record the energy consumption correctly over a period of time, periodic test schedules are usually followed where each meter in service is compared with a **portable standard** meter, that is, a meter in which the error has been reduced to a minimum.

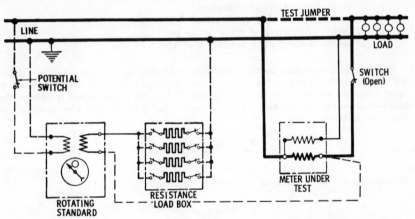

Testing Circuit for a Two-Wire Meter, Using a Resistance Load.

The size of error permitted may vary in different parts of the country but is usually around ±3 per cent of its rated load.

When setting up a meter for test, the current coils of the two meters, that is, of the portable standard and the meter under test, are connected in series, whereas their potential coils are connected in parallel.

During the test period, the revolutions of the standard are compared with the meter under test for the same interval of time, allowance being made in the calculations for the disc constant of the two meters.

WATTHOUR-METER TEST

In cases where the load is unknown it may be determined by timing the standard with a stop watch and comparing the value of the watts from the expression,

$$\text{True watts} = \frac{3,600 \times \text{Revolutions} \times \text{Watthour Constant}}{\text{Time in seconds}} \qquad (1)$$

With reference to the test circuits the rotating standard is operated by a potential switch which stops and starts the standard, a reading of the standard is taken at the beginning and at the end of the test, and the difference between these two readings gives the number of revolutions of the standard.

If no correction is to be applied to the rotating standard, the per cent accuracy of the watthour meter under test is obtained from equation,

$$\text{Per cent accuracy} = \frac{k_h \times r}{K_h \times R} \qquad (2)$$

Where

r = revolutions of meter under test.
R = revolutions of rotating standard.
k_h = watthour constant of meter under test.
K_h = watthour constant of rotating standard.

The method shown may be facilitated by introducing an additional symbol, values for which may be given to the tester in tabular form. Thus, if R_0 = the number of revolutions the rotating standard should make when the tested meter is correct, the number of revolutions of two watthour meters for a given load vary inversely as their disc constants, then

$$\frac{R_0}{r} = \frac{k_h}{K_h} \text{ or } R_0 = \frac{k_h \times r}{K_h} \qquad (3)$$

Substituting R_0 in the equation for per cent accuracy, we obtain

$$\% \text{ accuracy} = \frac{R_0 \times 100}{r}$$

Example—In a certain test the rotating standard has a constant $K_h = 0.05$ and the watthour meter under test has a constant $k_h = 0.5$. If r, the number of revolutions of the meter under test, $= 2$, determine the number of revolutions of the rotating standard.

Solution—Substituting values in formula (3) we obtain

$$R_0 = \frac{k_h \times r}{K_h} = \frac{0.5 \times 2}{0.05} = 20.$$

That is, for 2 revolutions of the meter under test, the standard should make 20 revolutions.

WATTHOUR-METER TEST

Example—Assume the rotating standard in the previous example actually made 20.24 revolutions, what is the accuracy of the watthour meter under test?

Solution

$$\text{Per cent accuracy} = \frac{R_0 \times 100}{r} = \frac{20 \times 100}{20.24} = 98.8\%.$$

This actually means that the meter is 1.2% slow and should be speeded up slightly.

Example—In a test of a DC 15 ampere watthour meter, the corrected average volt and ampere readings are 220 and 14.75, respectively. During the test interval 38 revolutions are counted in 53.5 seconds and the meter constant is 1.25. What is the per cent accuracy of the meter at this load?

Solution—Average standard watts

$$W_1 = 14.75 \times 220 = 3,245$$

Inserting our values in equation (1) we obtain the average meter watts as

$$W = \frac{3,600 \times 38 \times 1.25}{53.5} = 3,196$$

$$\text{Meter accuracy} = \frac{W}{W_1} = \frac{3,196}{3,245} = 0.985 \text{ or } 98.5\%.$$

Other well known methods used in testing of watthour meters are: (1) **the indicating instrument method** and (2) **the stroboscopic method.** In the former, load is applied to the meter and watthours are measured by means of indicating instruments and timing devices such as stop watches or chronographs.

The ratio between the indicated or meter watthours and true watthours represents the accuracy of the meter under test, and is usually expressed in per cent.

The stroboscopic method involves the comparison of the speed of two similar discs, and utilizes a light source, a lens system, a photoelectric cell and amplifying equipment. This method of meter testing finds application in meter shops having a large number of meters to be tested. It is not limited to type of meter to be tested except that marking or slotting of the disc is necessary in order to obtain pulsating light.

WATTHOUR-METER TEST

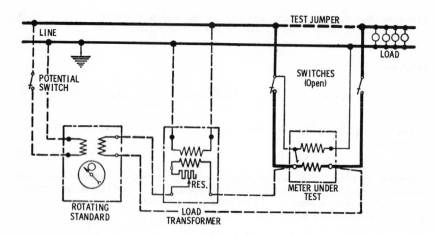

Testing Circuit for a Two-Wire Meter, Using a Loading Transformer—NOTE: Line side of meter may be left connected to service and potential jumper omitted. With such connections, secondary of loading transformer and current coil of rotating standard will be at line potential.

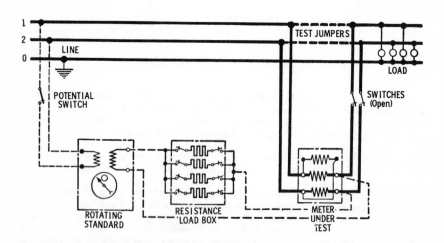

Testing Circuit for a Three-Wire, Single-Phase Meter, Using a Resistance Load on Line-to-Line Voltage.

POWER MEASUREMENT IN POLYPHASE SYSTEMS

Power Measurements with Two Wattmeters—With reference to connection diagram, the current coils of the meters should be in two of the lines and each potential coil connected from that line in which its current coil is placed, to the third line. The algebraic sum of the connected wattmeter readings gives the total wattage. That is, if the power factor of the load is unity, each wattmeter will read one half the total power. If the power factor is 50%, one wattmeter will read zero and the other will read the total power. If the power factor is somewhere between 50% and 100%, one wattmeter will read more than the other, in which case the total power is found by adding the two wattmeter readings. If the power factor is below 50% one wattmeter will indicate backwards. The connection of the current or voltage coil of this meter should be reversed in order that a reading may be obtained. In this case the power taken by the circuit is determined by subtracting the reading of the wattmeter that was reversed from the other wattmeter reading.

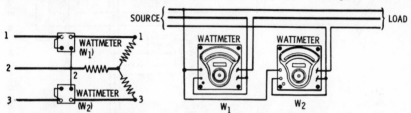

Power Factor Measurement—In a balanced three-phase circuit, the power factor may be obtained from the readings of the two wattmeters, without measuring the voltage or the amount of current of any of the circuits, by applying the following formula.

$$\tan \phi = \frac{W_1 - W_2}{W_1 + W_2} \sqrt{3}$$

Where ϕ = angle of lag; W_1 = reading on wattmeter indicating the larger amount of power; W_2 = reading on wattmeter indicating the smaller amount of power

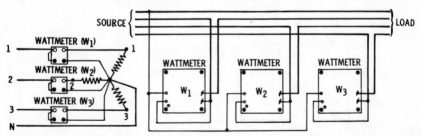

To measure the power in a three-phase, four-wire system, three wattmeters should be used and connected as shown. The current coils should be connected in the three lines and each potential coil should be connected from the line in which the current coil is placed to the neutral line. In this case wattmeter (W_1) measures the power taken by phase 1, wattmeter (W_2) the power taken by phase 2, etc. and the power is equal to the sum of the readings of the three meters.

CONNECTION OF WATTHOUR METER

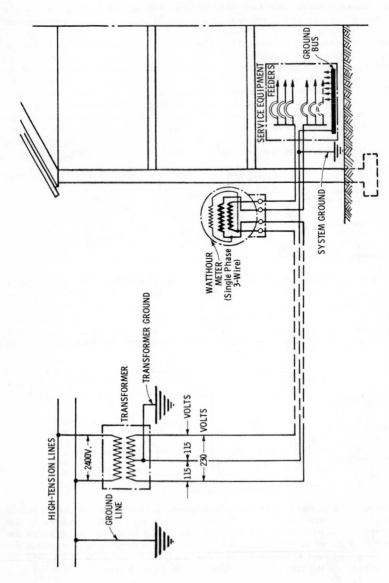

Typical Feeder Layout and Watthour Meter Connections for a Single-Phase, Three-Wire, 115/230 Volt AC System.

RELAYS
AND
INSTRUMENT
CONNECTIONS

OVERLOAD RELAY

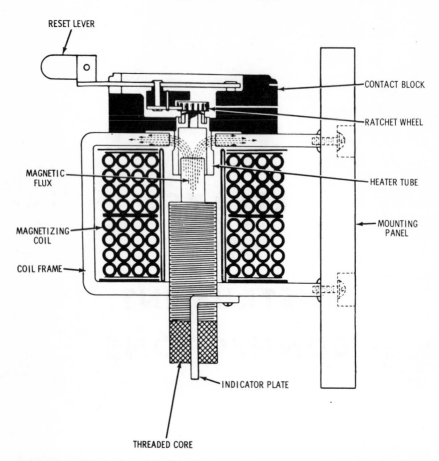

RESET LEVER

CONTACT BLOCK

RATCHET WHEEL

MAGNETIC FLUX

HEATER TUBE

MAGNETIZING COIL

MOUNTING PANEL

COIL FRAME

INDICATOR PLATE

THREADED CORE

Operation—The load current flowing through the magnetizing coil sets up a magnetic flux in the core. A current directly proportional to the load current is induced in the heater tube. Under overload conditions this current generates enough heat to melt the solder holding the ratchet wheel in place. When the ratchet wheel is released, a spring trips the relay and disconnects the load from the line. The relay may be reset by pushing the reset lever after allowing a short period of time for the solder to harden.

The tripping current is set by turning the threaded core to raise or lower the position of the core within the coil. A current-indicator plate indicates the correct current adjustment.

METHODS OF OVERLOAD PROTECTION WITH
INDUCTION-TYPE OVERLOAD RELAYS

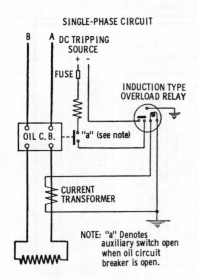

SINGLE-PHASE CIRCUIT

THREE-PHASE, THREE-WIRE CIRCUIT

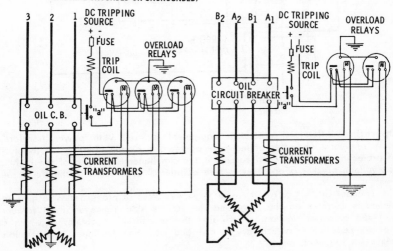

THREE-PHASE, THREE-WIRE CIRCUIT
(NEUTRAL GROUNDED OR UNGROUNDED)

TWO-PHASE, FOUR-WIRE CIRCUIT

NOTE: "a" Denotes auxiliary switch open when oil circuit breaker is open.

DIAGRAM OF CONNECTION FOR DIFFERENTIAL
PROTECTION OF POWER TRANSFORMERS

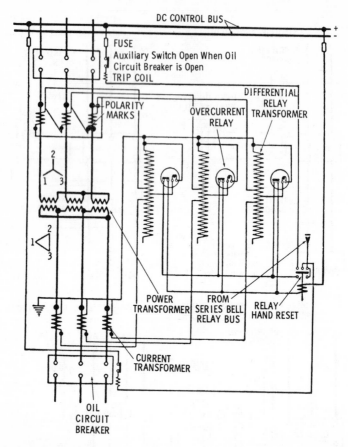

Operation—Differential protective equipment is used with power transformers most frequently when two or more are operated in parallel. Thus, when this system of protection is utilized both automatic and simultaneous tripping of the high- and low-voltage breaker is obtained in case of internal breakdown in the transformers.

It is important that current transformers be selected of proper ratios to give equal secondary currents on the high- and low-voltage side. However, most frequently the ratio of transformation is such that this is difficult to obtain, in which case taps are restored to, which may be changed from time to time. (For operation of relays see following page.)

CONNECTIONS FOR DIFFERENTIAL PROTECTION OF TRANSFORMER WITH A TERTIARY WINDING USING INDUCTION-TYPE OVERCURRENT RELAYS

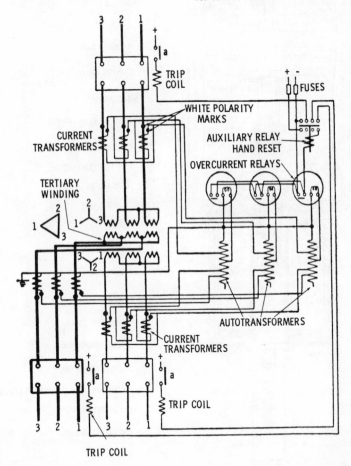

a: AUXILIARY SWITCH CLOSED WHEN OIL CIRCUIT BREAKER IS CLOSED

TRIP COIL

FUSES

WHITE POLARITY MARKS

CURRENT TRANSFORMERS

AUXILIARY RELAY HAND RESET

OVERCURRENT RELAYS

TERTIARY WINDING

AUTOTRANSFORMERS

CURRENT TRANSFORMERS

TRIP COIL

TRIP COIL

Operation—When due to internal faults in transformer windings the current through the overcurrent relays exceeds that for which the relays are set to operate, the relays close their contacts, in turn energizing the auxiliary relay coil, resulting in a simultaneous tripping of the three circuit breakers.

OVERCURRENT RELAY

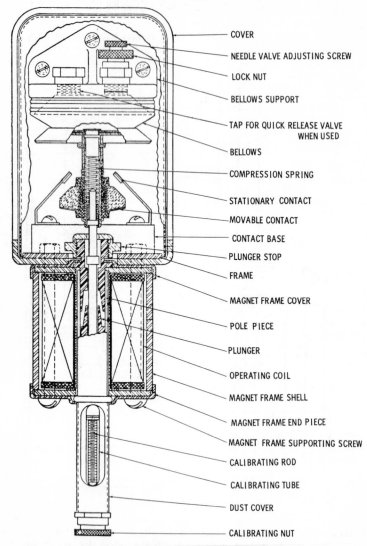

COVER

NEEDLE VALVE ADJUSTING SCREW

LOCK NUT

BELLOWS SUPPORT

TAP FOR QUICK RELEASE VALVE
WHEN USED

BELLOWS

COMPRESSION SPRING

STATIONARY CONTACT

MOVABLE CONTACT

CONTACT BASE

PLUNGER STOP

FRAME

MAGNET FRAME COVER

POLE PIECE

PLUNGER

OPERATING COIL

MAGNET FRAME SHELL

MAGNET FRAME END PIECE

MAGNET FRAME SUPPORTING SCREW

CALIBRATING ROD

CALIBRATING TUBE

DUST COVER

CALIBRATING NUT

SECTIONAL VIEW OF PLUNGER TYPE OVERCURRENT RELAY
FOR APPLICATION AND CONNECTIONS, SEE FOLLOWING PAGES

PLUNGER-TYPE OVERLOAD RELAY

Operation Principles—When due to certain conditions in the circuit to be protected, the current exceeds the value at which the relay is set to operate, the plunger raises and carries up with it the movable cone contact, or it strikes against the center of the toggle mechanisms (depending upon the type of contacts in the relay) thus causing the contacts to function.

Generally, when a relay functions to open its contacts it is referred to as a **circuit-opening** type, and when it functions to close its contacts, it is referred to as the **circuit-closing** type. In this manner the function of the contacts of a relay is most frequently used as a means of identification, a relay being **circuit-closing** or **circuit-opening,** or **circuit-opening** and **circuit-closing.**

Timing Features—In regard to speed of operation a relay may be referred to as instantaneous, or time delay. The word instantaneous is a general qualifying term applied to any relay, indicating that no delayed action has been purposely introduced.

The time relays are similar in construction to the instantaneous type, except for the addition of an air bellows which limits the rate of travel of the relay plunger, and in this way introduces an interval of time to the opening or closing of the relay contacts.

This time delay may be regulated to suit the special service desired, which is accomplished by means of a needle valve located in the head of the bellows as shown on page 80. This valve controls the rate of air flow from the bellows under various operating conditions.

METHODS OF OVERLOAD PROTECTION WITH PLUNGER-TYPE, CIRCUIT-CLOSING RELAYS

SINGLE-PHASE CIRCUIT

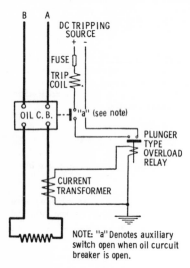

THREE-PHASE, THREE WIRE CIRCUIT

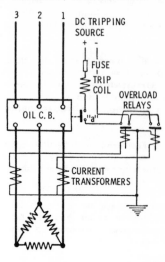

NOTE: "a" Denotes auxiliary switch open when oil circuit breaker is open.

THREE-PHASE, THREE WIRE CIRCUIT

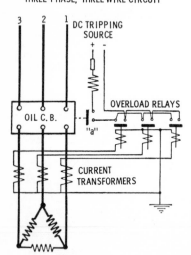

TWO-PHASE, FOUR WIRE CIRCUIT

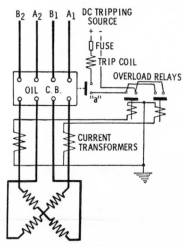

OVERLOAD PROTECTION WITH PLUNGER-
TYPE, CIRCUIT-OPENING RELAYS

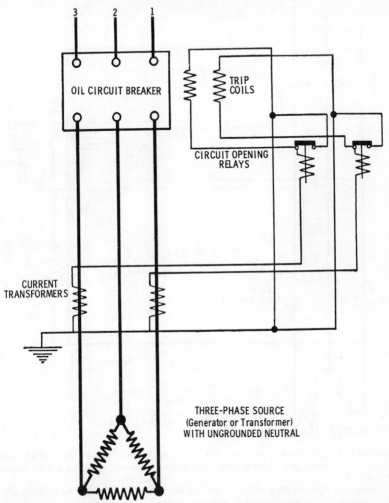

Operation—In this circuit overload protection is accomplished by means of a set of current transformers, with its associated relays and trip coils. The relay contacts are normally closed. When the overload through the trip coils exceeds that for which the relays are set to operate, the contacts open, placing the trip coils in series with the relay coils, causing the trip coils to trip the oil circuit breaker.

OVERLOAD PROTECTION WITH PLUNGER-TYPE, CIRCUIT-CLOSING RELAYS

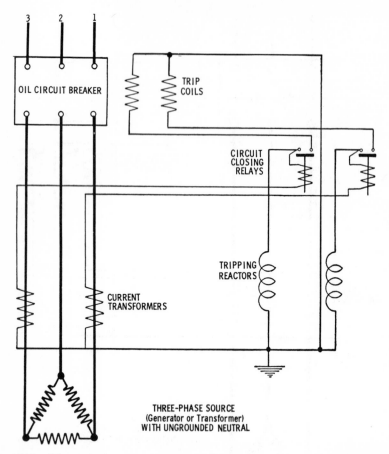

THREE-PHASE SOURCE
(Generator or Transformer)
WITH UNGROUNDED NEUTRAL

Operation—When tripping reactors are used as in overcurrent and other types of relays, instrument and meters should be connected from an extra set of current transformers.

Tripping reactors are frequently employed when a direct current or reliable alternating current is not available as a tripping source for the relays.

Normally the trip coil circuit is open and the reactor forms the closed circuit of the current transformer secondary. When the overload is of a sufficiently high value to cause operation of the relay, it closes the trip coil circuit in shunt with the reactor, causing sufficient current to be passed through the coils to trip the breaker.

TRIPPING OF TWO OIL CIRCUIT BREAKERS USING TRIPPING REACTORS AND CIRCUIT-CLOSING RELAYS

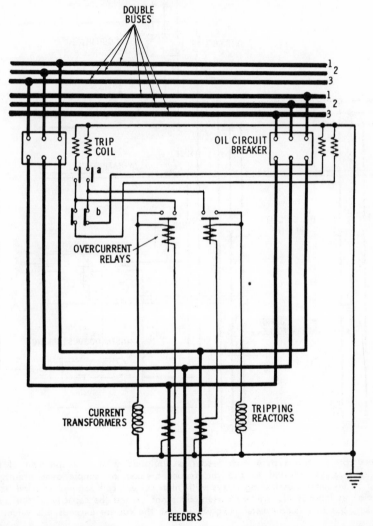

DOUBLE BUSES

TRIP COIL

OIL CIRCUIT BREAKER

a

b

OVERCURRENT RELAYS

CURRENT TRANSFORMERS

TRIPPING REACTORS

FEEDERS

Note—Auxiliary switch "a" is open when oil circuit breaker is open, and auxiliary switch "b" is closed when the oil circuit breaker is open.

APPLICATION OF LOCKING RELAYS TO FEEDER CIRCUITS

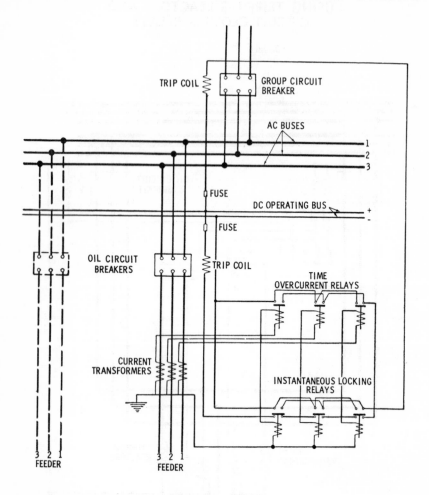

Operation—In this system each feeder is equipped with a complement of time overload relays adjusted to trip the feeder breaker on simple overcurrent, and a set of instantaneous locking relays with high current coil setting, adjusted not to function as long as the primary current does not exceed the capacity of the feeder breaker, but to function instantaneously in case the current exceeds this value.

The operation of the locking relays opens the tripping circuit of the feeder of the heavy duty group circuit breaker.

APPLICATION OF LOCKING RELAYS TO FEEDER CIRCUITS

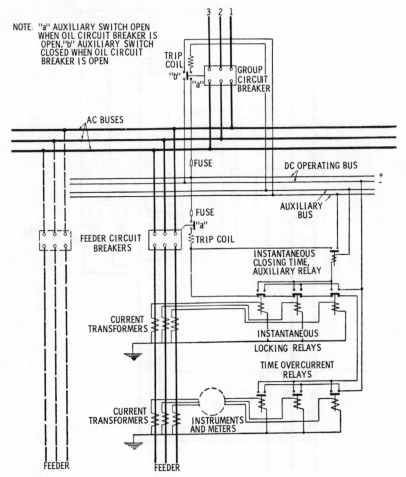

NOTE: "a" AUXILIARY SWITCH OPEN WHEN OIL CIRCUIT BREAKER IS OPEN."b" AUXILIARY SWITCH CLOSED WHEN OIL CIRCUIT BREAKER IS OPEN

3 2 1

TRIP COIL

"b" "a"

GROUP CIRCUIT BREAKER

AC BUSES

FUSE

DC OPERATING BUS

+ −

FUSE
"a"
TRIP COIL

AUXILIARY BUS

FEEDER CIRCUIT BREAKERS

INSTANTANEOUS CLOSING TIME, AUXILIARY RELAY

CURRENT TRANSFORMERS

INSTANTANEOUS

LOCKING RELAYS

TIME OVERCURRENT RELAYS

CURRENT TRANSFORMERS

INSTRUMENTS AND METERS

FEEDER

FEEDER

Operation—In this, as in the system shown on the previous page, the locking relays operate only upon excessive overcurrent, in which case the locking relays close the feeder breaker and open the group breaker.

An additional relay equipped with a direct current coil arranged to close instantaneously and reset itself (open) in a definite time is used as an auxiliary relay to work in conjunction with a circuit closing auxiliary switch on the group breaker to open the feeder breaker after the group breaker has been opened.

OVERLOAD-RELAY CONNECTION

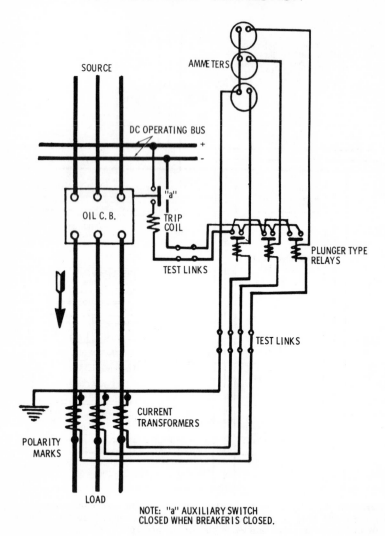

SOURCE

AMMETERS

DC OPERATING BUS

"a"

TRIP COIL

OIL C. B.

TEST LINKS

PLUNGER TYPE RELAYS

TEST LINKS

CURRENT TRANSFORMERS

POLARITY MARKS

LOAD

NOTE: "a" AUXILIARY SWITCH CLOSED WHEN BREAKER IS CLOSED.

OVERCURRENT PROTECTION

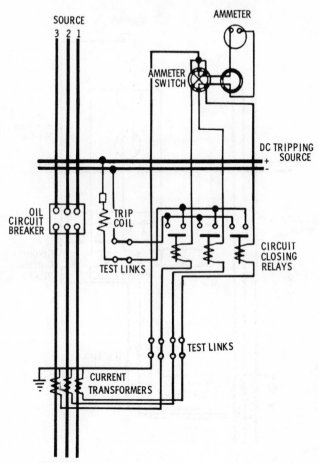

Overload Protection on Typical AC Feeder Circuit.

Operation—When current exceeds the setting of the relays, the relays will close their contacts, energizing the trip coil, which trips the oil circuit breaker.

The test links shown are optional but will, if used, facilitate the testing and calibration of instruments.

The current in each phase is measured by means of an ammeter and a three-way switch.

OVERCURRENT PROTECTION

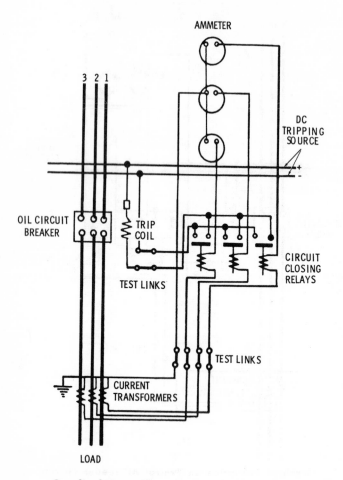

Overload Protection on Typical AC Feeder.

Operation—When current exceeds the setting of the relays, the relays will close their contacts, energizing the trip coil, which trips the oil circuit breaker.

The test links are optional but will, if used, facilitate testing or calibration of instruments.

The current in each phase is measured by individual ammeters.

OVERCURRENT PROTECTION

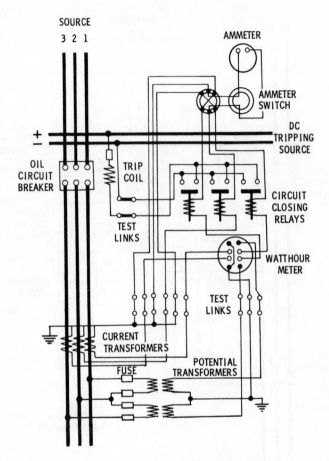

Overload Protection on Typical AC Feeder.

Operation—When current exceeds the setting of the relays, the relays will close their contacts, energizing the trip coil which trips the oil circuit breaker.

The energy is measured by means of a watthour meter; the current in each phase is measured by ammeter and three-way switch.

Test links shown are optional but will, if used, facilitate the testing of relays and instruments.

OVERLOAD PROTECTION

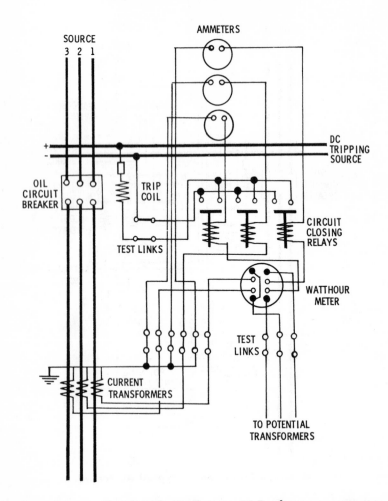

Overload Protection on AC Feeder.

Operation—When the current exceeds the setting of the relays, the relays will close their contacts, energizing the trip coil which trips the breaker.

The energy is measured by means of a watthour meter, and the current in each phase is measured by individual ammeters. Test links are optional but will, if used, facilitate the testing or calibration of relays and instruments.

OVERCURRENT PROTECTION

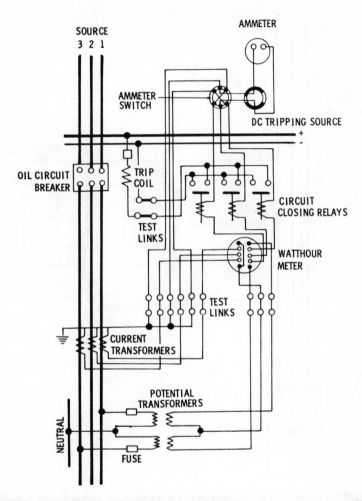

Operation—When current exceeds the setting of the relays, the relays will close their contacts, energizing the trip coil, which trips the oil circuit breaker. The energy is measured by a watthour meter, and the current in each phase is measured by ammeter and three-way switch.

Test links are optional but will, if used, facilitate the testing and calibration of relays and instrument.

TEMPERATURE OVERCURRENT PROTECTION

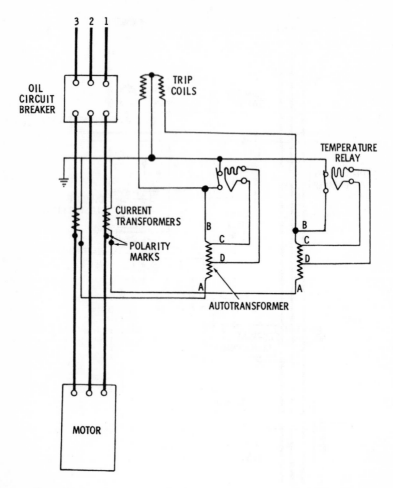

Temperature Overcurrent Protection for Synchronous Motor Using Tempera-ture Relays.

Operation—When the overcurrent exceeds the rating at which the relays are set to operate, the heating effect of the current passing through the relays will cause the relay contacts to close and energize the trip coils, which trips the oil circuit breaker. The relay operating characteristics are usually inverse-time, in that the time to operate the relay varies inversely with the overcurrent applied.

GROUND
DETECTOR
AND
CONNECTIONS

GROUND DETECTOR

On underground systems, AC as well as DC, it is necessary to install some kind of equipment for detecting or reading leakage to ground, in accord with the National Electrical Code.

For low-voltage two-wire systems, the simplest method is to connect two lamps of the system voltage in series across the two wires, with the connection between the two lamps grounded.

Ground on one side will obviously short circuit and darken the lamp on that side.

Above 300 volts, static or glover type of ground detectors are generally used. Standard connections for these detectors are shown on the following pages, as well as ground detection by voltmeter or lamp method.

Before connecting ground-detection instrument, compare operating voltage with that given on the meter; and in each case follow the manufacturers recommendation.

For example of ground-detection diagrams, see the following pages.

GROUND-DETECTOR CONNECTION

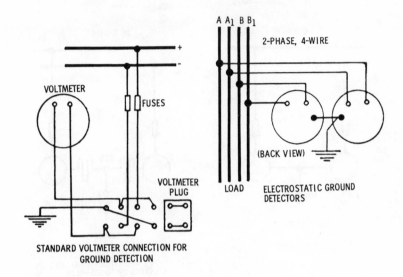

STANDARD VOLTMETER CONNECTION FOR
GROUND DETECTION

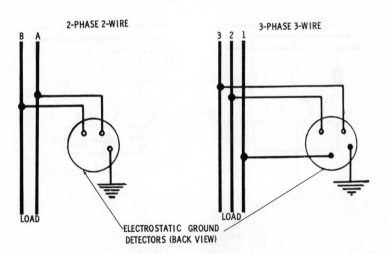

CONNECTION FOR GROUND DETECTION ON AC CIRCUITS, FOR VOLTAGES UP TO 3300.

GROUND-DETECTOR CONNECTION

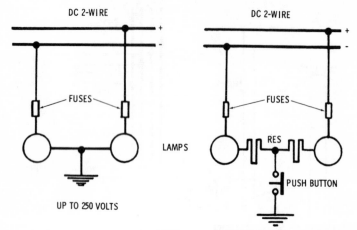

DC 2-WIRE

FUSES

LAMPS

UP TO 250 VOLTS

DC 2-WIRE

FUSES

RES

PUSH BUTTON

WITH PROPER LAMPS AND RESISTORS
THIS CONNECTION CAN BE USED ON
VOLTAGES UP TO 600 VOLTS

AC 3-PHASE 3-WIRE

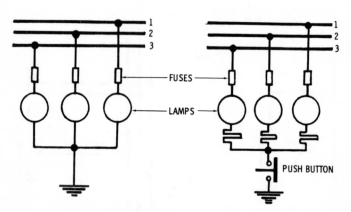

FUSES

LAMPS

PUSH BUTTON

WITH PROPER LAMPS AND RESISTORS
THIS CONNECTION CAN BE USED ON
VOLTAGE UP TO 650.

CONNECTION OF GROUND DETECTOR LAMPS ON AC AND DC CIRCUITS.

SWITCHBOARD
WIRING
DIAGRAMS

DC GENERATOR WIRING DIAGRAM

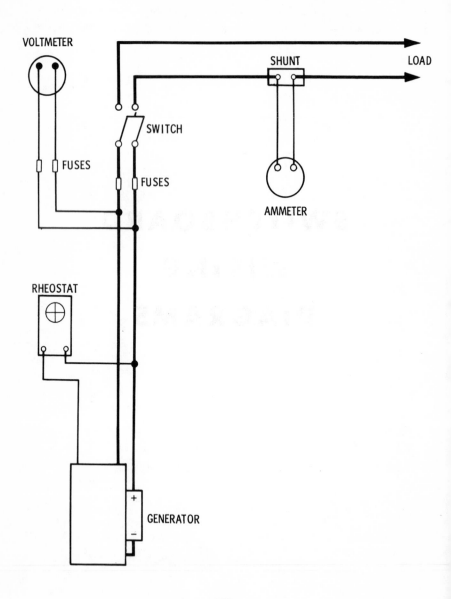

DIRECT-CURRENT GENERATOR CONNECTIONS

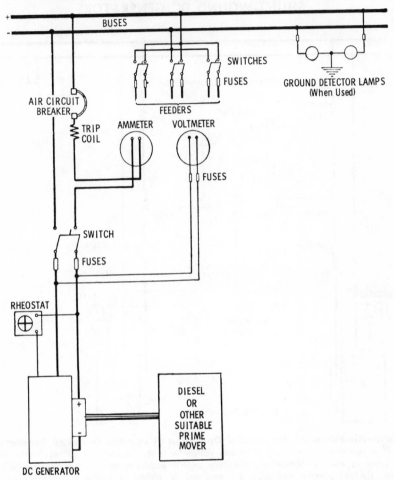

Connection of a Shunt-Wound Direct-Current Generator—The connections are largely self-explanatory, the voltmeter being connected across the main leads at the generator side of the double-pole knife switch. This will enable the operator to read the voltage of the machine at all times, regardless of the position of the main switches. The current indicator (ammeter) is connected in series with the positive lead connecting the machine to the load. The purpose of the overload coil on the circuit breaker is to prevent the current from reaching dangerous proportions, that is, when the current exceeds the calibrated settings of the coil, the breaker trips, disconnecting the generator from its load.

CONNECTION FOR PARALLEL OPERATION OF TWO SHUNT-WOUND DC GENERATORS

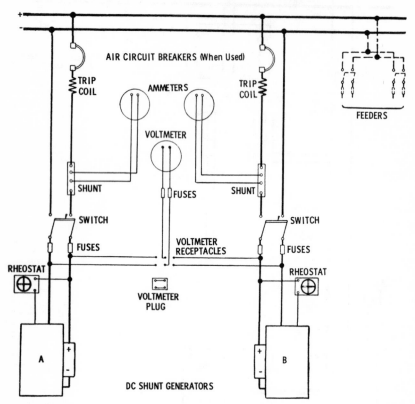

Connection diagram for Parallel Operation of Two Shunt-Wound Generators —It is customary to employ only one voltmeter with the addition of receptacles and a plug as shown. Sometimes a rotary switch arrangement is employed, in which .case the receptacles and plug are omitted. In either case, the voltmeter may be connected at will, to read the voltage across the terminals of any one of two or more generators. Occasionally voltage readings across the bus-bars (load) may be included in the voltmeter-switch arrangement. The method for operating the two generators in parallel is as follows: Assume that generator **B,** by means of its prime mover has been brought up to normal speed and is already connected to the bus-bars. Then with the switch and circuit breaker of **A** open, start the prime mover of **A,** and bring it up to speed. Now adjust the field rheostat of **A,** and note the voltmeter reading on this machine. Finally close the circuit breaker and switch of generator **A.**

PARALLEL OPERATION OF 2 DC COMPOUND GENERATORS

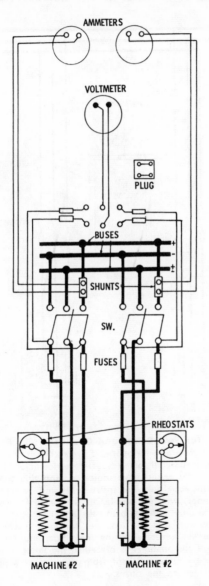

CONNECTION FOR PARALLEL OPERATION OF TWO COMPOUND-WOUND DC GENERATORS

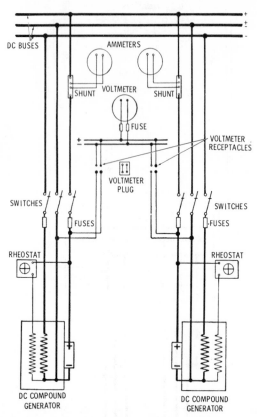

Detail of Connections for Two Compound Generators in Parallel—When two over-compounded generators are to be operated in parallel, it is necessary for a satisfactory division of loads, to parallel their respective series fields. This is accomplished by connecting their negatives together as indicated, and this common connector is usually referred to as the equalizer. The instruments and switches shown are connected in the usual manner, which is similar to that used for connection of shunt generators in parallel, the only addition being the equalizer and connections thereto. It should be noted, however, that the ammeter for each machine should be connected in the lead from the armature to the main bus, and not in the lead from the series field, because if the ammeter is placed in the latter it will read the series field current which may be quite different from the current supplied by the generator to the load connected to the buses.

3-WIRE DC GENERATOR DIAGRAM

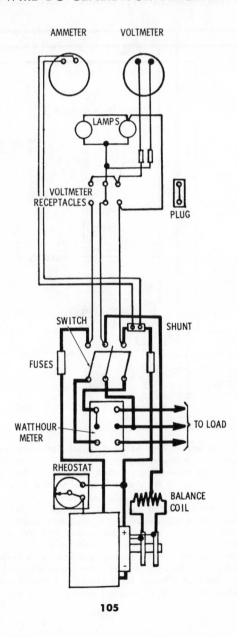

AMMETER   VOLTMETER

LAMPS

VOLTMETER
RECEPTACLES

PLUG

SWITCH   SHUNT

FUSES

WATTHOUR
METER

TO LOAD

RHEOSTAT

BALANCE
COIL

+

−

DIRECT-CURRENT, THREE-WIRE GENERATOR

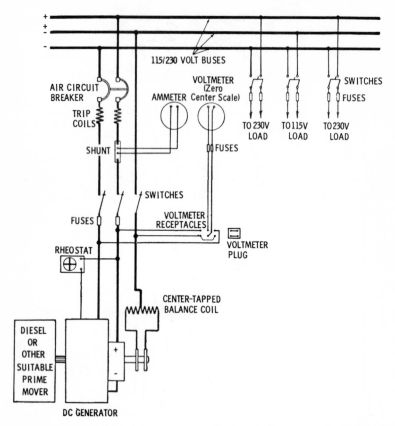

The three-wire generator with external balance coil is often resorted to when it is desired to obtain a three-wire system with a minimum of rotating machinery. The third wire (sometimes misleadingly called neutral) is obtained as follows: To an ordinary generator designed to give a terminal voltage equal to that between the two main wires, are added two slip rings as shown; from these slip rings two leads are brought out and connected to armature points located 180 electrical degrees apart (this connection is not shown in the diagram). Collectors from the slip rings are connected from the two ends of the balance coil wound on an iron core, and the middle point of this coil is finally connected to the third wire. It should be observed that in a system of this kind it is necessary to balance the load between the two main wires and the wire leading from the balance coil as closely as possible. The amount of unbalance allowed for a properly designed system (usually specified by the manufacturers) should not exceed approximately 10% of the total current.

WIRING DIAGRAM OF TYPICAL AC FEEDER PANEL

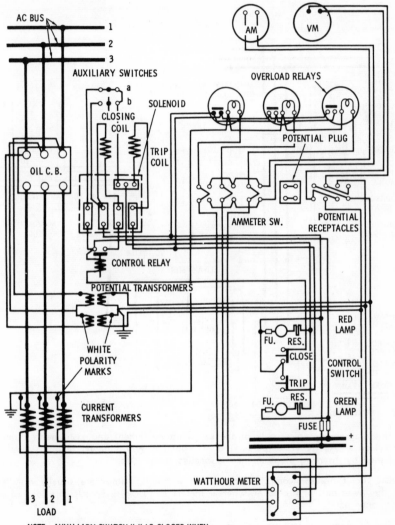

NOTE: AUXILIARY SWITCH "a" IS CLOSED WHEN
OIL CIRCUIT BREAKER IS CLOSED.

AUXILIARY SWITCH "b" IS OPEN WHEN
OIL CIRCUIT BREAKER IS CLOSED.

WIRING DIAGRAM FOR TYPICAL AC GENERATOR

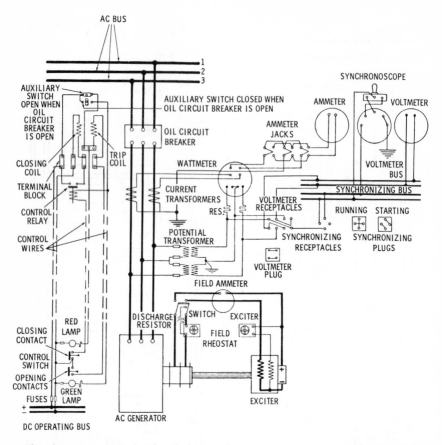

This diagram is typical only of the switching equipment and instruments usually found on an AC generator panel. The AC voltmeter and ammeter readings may be obtained by inserting plugs in their respective receptacles.

Oil circuit breaker control switches and indicating lamps are usually installed on the lower part of the panel, whereas meters and plug receptacles are located on the upper part.

The AC generator voltage may be controlled from two points:

(1) By the exciter field rheostat which controls the terminal voltage of the exciter or (2) By the AC generator field rheostat which varies the resistance of the AC generator field circuit.

CONNECTION FOR DC OPERATED SOLENOID USED
FOR CONTROL OF DC OIL CIRCUIT BREAKER

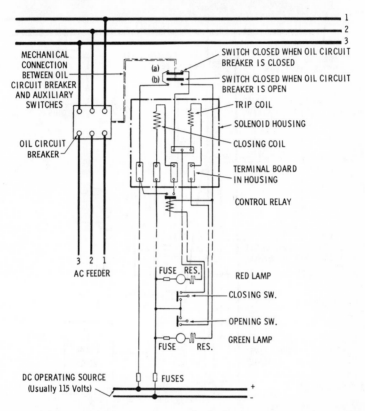

Typical Connection Diagram for a Remote Controlled Oil Circuit Breaker—In this method of operation, it is necessary, however, that an unfailing supply of direct current be available. The operation of the breaker is accomplished as follows: Assume the breaker is open and the condition for its closing has been established. When the main breaker is open, auxiliary switch marked (b) is closed, and the green lamp on the instrument board is lighted. When the closing switch is operated, the coil of the control relay whose contacts are normally open, becomes energized and closes its contact. This in turn actuates the closing coil (which is mechanically connected with the breaker contacts) closing the breaker. This closing of the breaker simultaneously reverses the position of the auxiliary switches, opening the previously closed switch marked (b) and closes switch marked (a), which in turn extinguishes the green lamp and lights the red. The breaker may be opened in a similar manner by operating the lower of the two switches on the control board.

ELECTROLYTIC GENERATOR WITH POLARITY-DIRECTIONAL PROTECTION

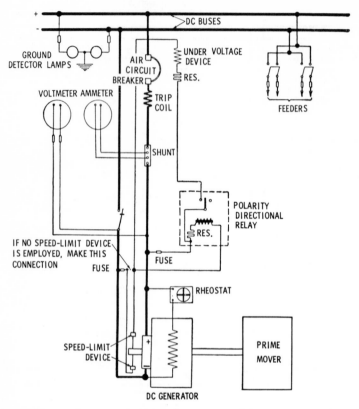

Polarity directional protection such as that which may be used where protection against sparks is of the utmost importance, as, for example, where hydrogen or other high explosive materials are manufactured. In such cases it is of the utmost importance that the polarity is not inverted, as the explosion resulting from such a condition might endanger both life and property. The polarity-directional relay consists essentially of a pair of stationary permanent magnets, a rotatable soft iron armature pivoted within a stationary coil and a double-throw set of contacts. The winding of the coil is of such direction that when potential is applied, connected with the proper polarity, the armature tends to rotate in a direction to keep the contacts closed to one side. A spring, in tension, tends to pull the armature back, open the closed contacts, and close the contacts on the other side. When an inversion of the polarity occurs, the spring overcomes the action of the magnet, which opens the circuit breaker.

UNDERVOLTAGE DEVICE AND DIAGRAMS

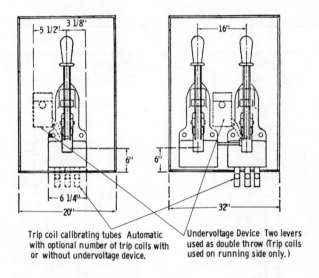

Trip coil calibrating tubes Automatic with optional number of trip coils with or without undervoltage device.

Undervoltage Device Two levers used as double throw (Trip coils used on running side only.)

OIL CIRCUIT BREAKER OPERATING LEVERS AND PANEL WIDTHS

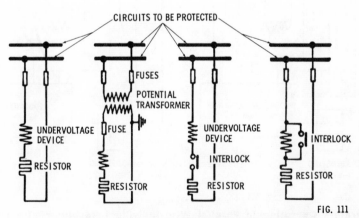

CIRCUITS TO BE PROTECTED

FUSES

POTENTIAL TRANSFORMER

UNDERVOLTAGE DEVICE

FUSE

UNDERVOLTAGE DEVICE

UNDERVOLTAGE DEVICE

INTERLOCK

RESISTOR

RESISTOR

INTERLOCK

RESISTOR

RESISTOR

INTERLOCK

RESISTOR

FIG. 111

METHODS OF CONNECTION FOR UNDERVOLTAGE DEVICE ATTACHMENTS

GENERATORS

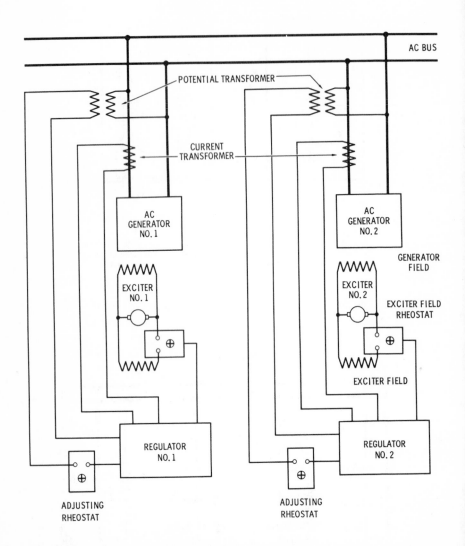

Generators Operating in Parallel With Individual Regulators—The division of reactive kilovolt-amperes between machines is automatic because of the compensation of the regulator from a current transformer.

GENERATORS

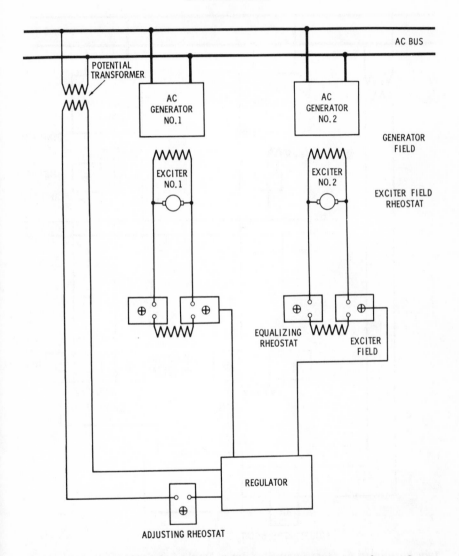

Generators Operating in Parallel Controlled by a Common Regulator—Output voltage is controlled automatically, but the division of load between generators must be done manually by adjustment of the equalizing rheostats.

GENERATORS

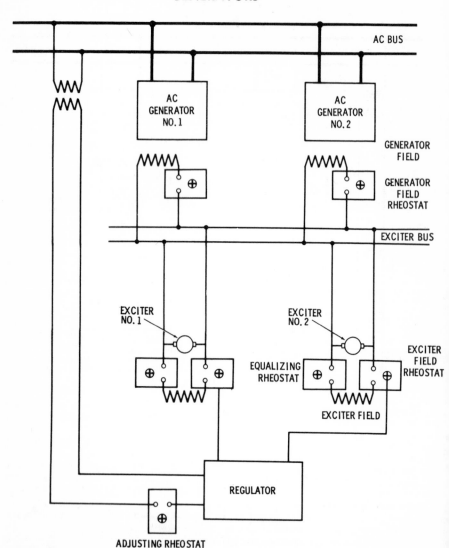

Two Paralleled Exciters Controlled by a Single Regulator—Output voltage is controlled automatically, but load division must be controlled manually by adjustment of the generator field rheostats.

DIRECT-CURRENT GENERATORS IN THREE-WIRE SERVICE

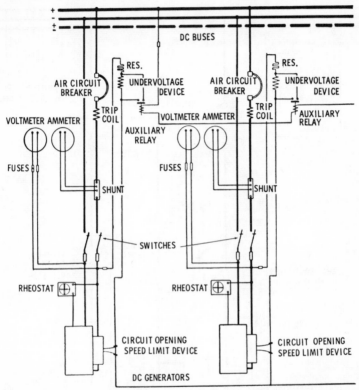

Common Method of Obtaining Three-Wire Service by Means of a Small Motor-Generator of Identical Size, Usually Identified as a Balancer Set—The additional wire or the so-called neutral is obtained and brought out from the common lead in the balancer set connecting the positive of one machine with the negative of the other. By the employment of a system of this kind, it is possible to establish better economy, in that the higher potential between the main generators positive and negative leads can be utilized for power service. The amount of this saving in copper may best be understood by the fact that the weight of the connectors (and therefore the cost) required to transmit a given amount of power at a given efficiency is inversely proportional to the square of the line voltage. When establishing such a system, however, it is necessary to employ some protective scheme to guard against the unbalance of voltage in case the balancer set should become disconnected. The voltage differential relay shown, will protect against unbalanced voltage, and as this relay is practically instantaneous in action, will protect against false operation caused by transitory disturbances. Definite time limit relays are utilized in the contact circuits.

METHOD OF UNBALANCED VOLTAGE PROTECTION

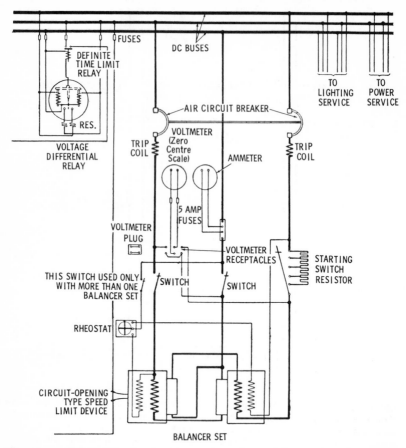

BALANCER SET

The voltage differential relay functions principally as follows: The relay consists essentially of a pair of solenoids of equal characteristics, and each with a plunger core connected to a balanced lever which actuates the contacts. One winding is connected across one circuit and the other winding across the other circuit of the two circuits to be differentially protected. As long as the voltages are equal, the balance lever is in equilibrium and the contacts remain open. When for any reason the voltage becomes unequal, the unequal pull of the two solenoids tends to close the contacts and when this difference in voltage reaches the value at which the relay is calibrated, the contacts close instantaneously energizing the definite time limit and auxiliary relays, which in turn shorts the coil of undervoltage device on the circuit breakers, tripping the breakers and disconnects the generators from the buses.

CIRCUIT BREAKER ARRANGEMENT AND DIAGRAMS

REMOTE-CONTROLLED CIRCUIT BREAKER

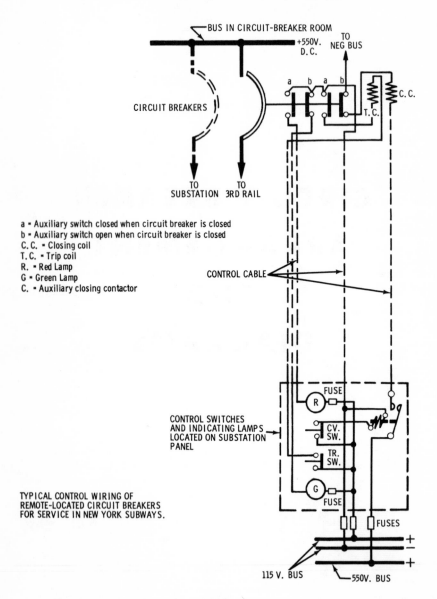

BUS IN CIRCUIT-BREAKER ROOM

+550V. D.C.

TO NEG BUS

CIRCUIT BREAKERS

C.C.

T.C.

TO SUBSTATION   TO 3RD RAIL

a = Auxiliary switch closed when circuit breaker is closed
b = Auxiliary switch open when circuit breaker is closed
C.C. = Closing coil
T.C. = Trip coil
R. = Red Lamp
G = Green Lamp
C. = Auxiliary closing contactor

CONTROL CABLE

CONTROL SWITCHES
AND INDICATING LAMPS
LOCATED ON SUBSTATION
PANEL

FUSE

R

CV. SW.

TR. SW.

G

FUSE

TYPICAL CONTROL WIRING OF
REMOTE-LOCATED CIRCUIT BREAKERS
FOR SERVICE IN NEW YORK SUBWAYS.

FUSES

115 V. BUS

550V. BUS

118

AIR CIRCUIT BREAKER

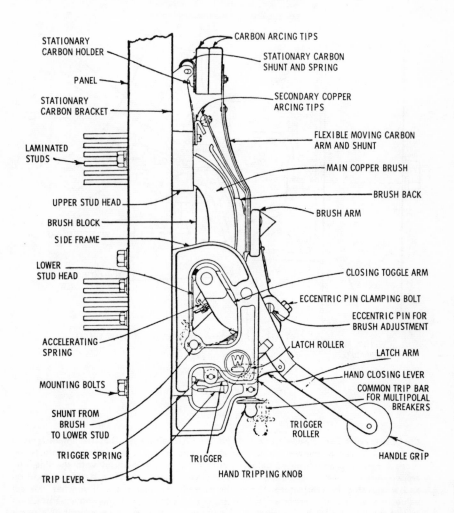

STATIONARY
CARBON HOLDER

CARBON ARCING TIPS

STATIONARY CARBON
SHUNT AND SPRING

PANEL

STATIONARY
CARBON BRACKET

SECONDARY COPPER
ARCING TIPS

LAMINATED
STUDS

FLEXIBLE MOVING CARBON
ARM AND SHUNT

MAIN COPPER BRUSH

BRUSH BACK

UPPER STUD HEAD

BRUSH ARM

BRUSH BLOCK

SIDE FRAME

LOWER
STUD HEAD

CLOSING TOGGLE ARM

ECCENTRIC PIN CLAMPING BOLT

ECCENTRIC PIN FOR
BRUSH ADJUSTMENT

LATCH ROLLER

LATCH ARM

ACCELERATING
SPRING

HAND CLOSING LEVER

COMMON TRIP BAR
FOR MULTIPOLAR
BREAKERS

MOUNTING BOLTS

SHUNT FROM
BRUSH
TO LOWER STUD

TRIGGER
ROLLER

TRIGGER SPRING

TRIGGER

HANDLE GRIP

TRIP LEVER

HAND TRIPPING KNOB

Principal Parts of 3,000-4,000 Ampere Carbon Circuit Breaker Without Overload Trip.

AIR CIRCUIT BREAKER

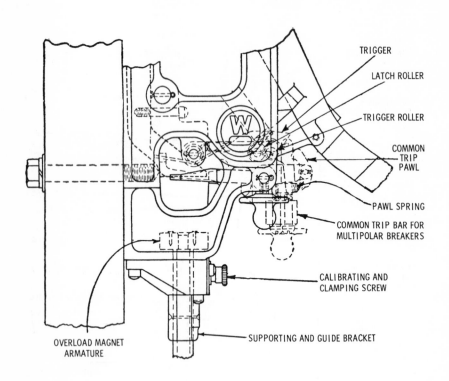

TRIGGER

LATCH ROLLER

TRIGGER ROLLER

COMMON TRIP PAWL

PAWL SPRING

COMMON TRIP BAR FOR MULTIPOLAR BREAKERS

CALIBRATING AND CLAMPING SCREW

SUPPORTING AND GUIDE BRACKET

OVERLOAD MAGNET ARMATURE

Carbon Circuit Breaker with Overload Trip Attachment—The attachment is used to trip a breaker whenever the current in the circuit which the breaker protects exceeds a certain predetermined value. It consists of a coil in series with the line, the ampere-turns of which act on a magnetic circuit consisting of a stationary portion and a movable iron armature. When the current through the coil reaches the set value, the armature is attracted to the stationary portion and this movement serves to trip the breaker latch. The amount of current required in the series coil of a given overload trip device to cause it to trip the breaker is dependent on the air gap between the movable armature and the stationary magnet. Various tripping points can be obtained by varying this gap.

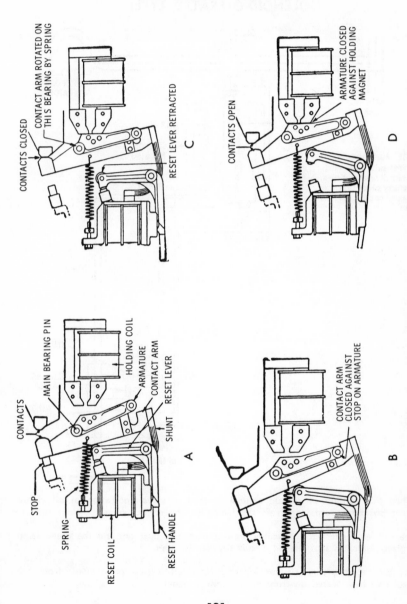

High-Speed-Trip Circuit Breaker Showing Operation of the Resetting Mechanism.

REMOTE-CONTROL WIRING FOR OIL CIRCUIT BREAKER
(SOLENOID-OPERATED TYPE)

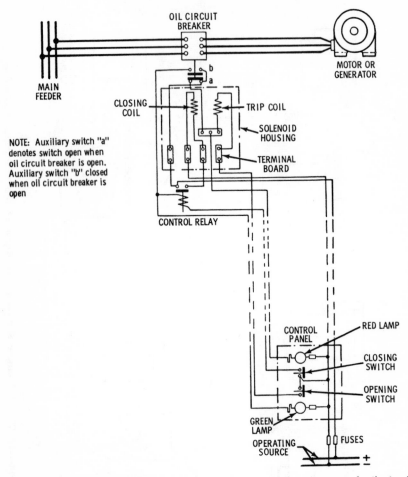

When this method of remote control is used, a visual indication of oil circuit breaker position is obtained from the lamps on the control panel.

The red lamp energized indicates breaker in closed position, and the green lamp energized indicates that the oil circuit breaker is open.

The oil circuit breaker is conveniently operated (closed or opened) from the control switches located on front of the control panel.

SOLENOID-OPERATED OIL CIRCUIT BREAKER

NOTE: a = Auxiliary switch closed when oil circuit breaker
is closed.
b = Auxiliary switch open when breaker is closed.

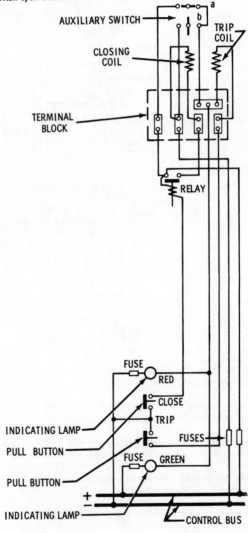

MOTOR MECHANISM FOR OIL CIRCUIT BREAKER

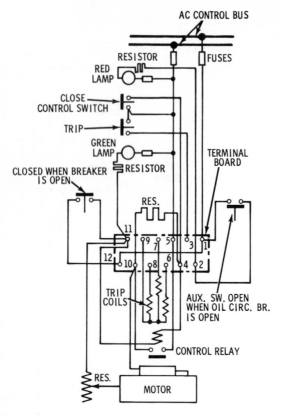

The breaker is closed by means of a pull-button switch which completes the circuit of the control relay.

The control relay in turn energizes the motor of the mechanism, and seals itself to insure complete closing operation.

As the motor of the mechanism increases in speed the flyweights move outward, away from the driving shaft, and pull downward the toggle mechanism to close the breaker. This action raises the counterweight, which returns to its normal position after the breaker opens and resets the toggle mechanism for the next closing operation.

The circuit breaker at all times trips free from the mechanism, and is normally tripped by overload trip coils.

OIL CIRCUIT BREAKER WIRING

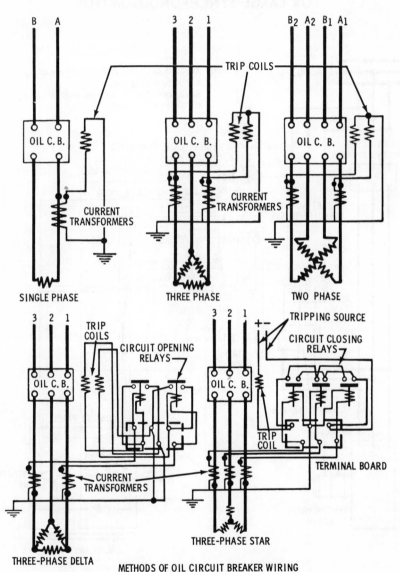

SINGLE PHASE

THREE PHASE

TWO PHASE

THREE-PHASE DELTA

THREE-PHASE STAR

METHODS OF OIL CIRCUIT BREAKER WIRING
WITH AND WITHOUT OVERCURRENT RELAYS

OIL CIRCUIT BREAKERS AND CONTROL ARRANGEMENT
FOR LARGE SYNCHRONOUS MOTOR

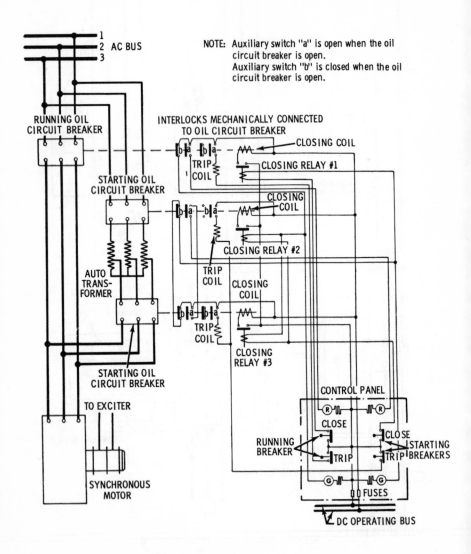

NOTE: Auxiliary switch "a" is open when the oil
circuit breaker is open.
Auxiliary switch "b" is closed when the oil
circuit breaker is open.

AC AND DC
GENERATOR
AND
MOTOR
DIAGRAMS

TERMINAL MARKINGS AND CONNECTIONS FOR DIRECT-CURRENT MOTORS AND GENERATORS

Marking of Terminals—The purpose of applying markings to the terminals of electric power apparatus according to a standard is to aid in making up connections to other parts of the electric power system, and to avoid improper connection that may result in unsatisfactory operation or damage.

Location of Markings—The markings are placed on or directly adjacent to terminals to which connections must be made from outside circuits, or from auxiliary devices which must be disconnected in order to facilitate shipments from the manufacturer.

Precautions—Although the system of terminal markings with letters and subscript numbers gives information, facilitating the connections of electrical machinery, there is the possibility of finding the terminals marked without system or according to some system other than standard (especially on old machinery or machinery of foreign manufacture). There is a further possibility that internal connections have been changed or that errors were made in markings. It is therefore advisable, before connecting apparatus to power supply systems, to make a check test for phase rotation, phase relation, polarity and equality of potential.

Subscript Numerals on Direct-Current Machinery Terminals—As applied to the terminals of direct-current windings of generators, motors and synchronous converters, the subscript numerals indicate the direction of current flow in the windings. Thus, with standard direction of rotation and polarity, the current in all windings will be flowing from 1 to 2, or from a lower to a higher subnumber.

Direction of Rotation for DC Motors—Connections shown on the following pages will give the standard **counter-clockwise** rotation facing the end opposite the drive. To obtain the opposite direction, or **clockwise** rotation, the **armature or main field leads must be reversed.**

Direction of Rotation for DC Generators—The standard direction of rotation for DC generators is **clockwise** when facing the end of machine opposite the drive, usually the commutator end of the machine. Direct-current generators with connections properly made up for standard rotation (clockwise) will not function if driven counter-clockwise, as any small current delivered by the armature tends to demagnetize the fields and thus prevents the armature from delivering current. If conditions call for reversed rotation, connections should be made up with either the armature leads transposed or the field leads transposed.

TERMINAL MARKINGS AND CONNECTIONS FOR
DIRECT-CURRENT MOTORS AND GENERATORS
—continued

Motor Generators—Any direct-current machine can be used either as a generator or as a motor. For desired direction of rotation, connection changes may be necessary and should be accomplished as previously described. The conventions for current flow in combination with the standardization of opposite directions of rotation for direct-current generators and direct-current motors works out so that any direct-current machine can be termed **generator** or **motor** without change in terminal markings. A direct-current motor or a direct-current generator, by direct coupling constitutes a motor generator. With such coupling, direction of rotation of motor and generator are necessarily reversed when each is from the **end opposite the drive.** The standard clockwise rotation for direct-current motors meets such coupling requirements without change in standard connections or rotation for either direct-current machine.

Coupling of AC and DC Motors and Generators—In the same manner as that already described for direct-current motors and generators, a direct-current motor may be coupled to an alternating-current generator without changing from the standard in either individual machine. When, however, the coupling of an alternating-current motor to a direct-current generator becomes necessary, this coupling cannot be made without rotation other than standard for one of the two machines. Since the rotation of the alternating-current machine is usually the more simply changed, it is general practice to operate a motor generator with clockwise rotation viewed from the generator end.

Example on How to Change Direction of Rotation in a DC Motor—When brushes are set for standard counter-clockwise rotation, it will be necessary to change assembly of brush holders for trailing operation. With reference to page 132 showing diagram and connections of a typical motor, proceed as follows: 1. Change connection as shown for clockwise rotation. 2. To change assembly of brush holders for trailing operation, first lock the armature in position of one brush on the commutator surface. Mark the brush holder stud of this brush X and studs of the opposite polarity Y. Raise all brushes in the holders, remove holders from the studs and reassemble them on the same studs in the reverse direction. Lower brush holders until the distance between the bodies and commutator surface is 3/32 in. then shift brush holder yoke until the nearest brush from either stud Y exactly fits over the space previously occupied by the brush X. The leads from the brush holder studs, one from the commutating fields and the other from the terminal board (lead A_1), should be interchanged in the studs. Erase paint mark on bearing housing and make a new mark to line up with the mark on the brush yoke.

TERMINAL MARKINGS AND CONNECTIONS
FOR DC SHUNT-WOUND MOTOR

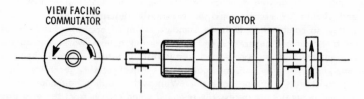

VIEW FACING COMMUTATOR

ROTOR

STANDARD DIRECTION OF ROTATION COUNTERCLOCKWISE
WHEN FACING COMMUTATOR END OF MOTOR

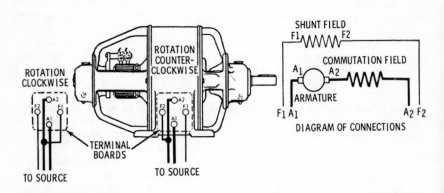

ROTATION CLOCKWISE

ROTATION COUNTER-CLOCKWISE

TERMINAL BOARDS

TO SOURCE

TO SOURCE

SHUNT FIELD

COMMUTATION FIELD

ARMATURE

DIAGRAM OF CONNECTIONS

The above drawings represent a typical shunt-wound motor, with terminal connections for either the standard counter-clockwise rotation or clockwise rotation, which sometimes is utilized to facilitate the proper functioning of machinery to be operated.

All motor and control wiring should be carefully installed in accordance with the National Electrical Code and any local requirements, and should be of ample capacity based on a maximum line voltage drop of 2 per cent at full load current.

Before operation, make sure that voltage on motor and control nameplates corresponds with that of power supply.

TERMINAL MARKINGS AND CONNECTIONS
FOR DC COMPOUND-WOUND MOTORS

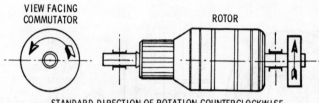

VIEW FACING COMMUTATOR

ROTOR

STANDARD DIRECTION OF ROTATION COUNTERCLOCKWISE WHEN FACING COMMUTATOR END OF MOTOR.

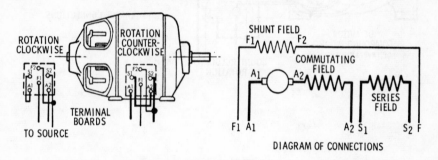

ROTATION CLOCKWISE

ROTATION COUNTER-CLOCKWISE

TERMINAL BOARDS

TO SOURCE

SHUNT FIELD

F1   F2

COMMUTATING FIELD

A1   A2

SERIES FIELD

F1 A1   A2 S1   S2 F

DIAGRAM OF CONNECTIONS

TYPICAL CONNECTION DIAGRAM FOR COMPOUND-WOUND MOTOR

Operation of Motors—Before placing the motor in service for the first time the following precautions should be observed:

Dry out all moisture. If the motor has been exposed to moist atmosphere for a long time while in transit or storage (or has been idle for a long period after installation in moist atmosphere) it should always be dried out thoroughly before being placed in service. If possible, place the motor in an oven and bake at a temperature not exceeding 85°C.

Fair results can be obtained by enclosing the motor with canvas or other covering, inserting some heating units or incandescent lamps to raise the temperature, and leaving a hole at the top of the enclosure to permit the escape of moisture. The motor may also be dried out by passing a current at low voltage (motor at rest) through the field windings to raise the temperature but not to exceed 85°C. The heat should be raised gradually until the whole winding is of this uniform temperature.

TERMINAL MARKINGS AND CONNECTIONS FOR STANDARD AND CLOCKWISE ROTATION

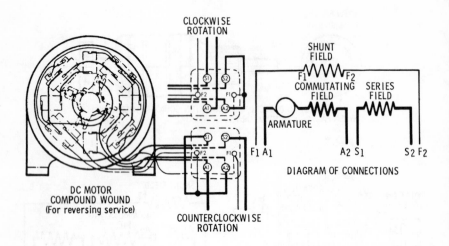

DC MOTOR
COMPOUND WOUND
(For reversing service)

CLOCKWISE
ROTATION

COUNTERCLOCKWISE
ROTATION

SHUNT
FIELD

COMMUTATING
FIELD

SERIES
FIELD

ARMATURE

F1 A1   A2 S1   S2 F2

DIAGRAM OF CONNECTIONS

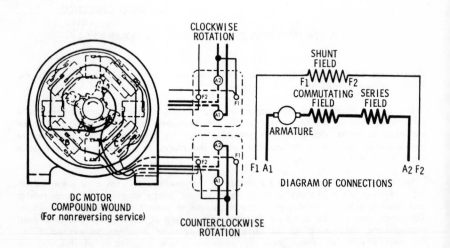

DC MOTOR
COMPOUND WOUND
(For nonreversing service)

CLOCKWISE
ROTATION

COUNTERCLOCKWISE
ROTATION

SHUNT
FIELD

COMMUTATING
FIELD

SERIES
FIELD

ARMATURE

F1 A1   A2 F2

DIAGRAM OF CONNECTIONS

STARTING RHEOSTAT AND CONNECTION DIAGRAM
FOR DC COMPOUND-WOUND MOTOR

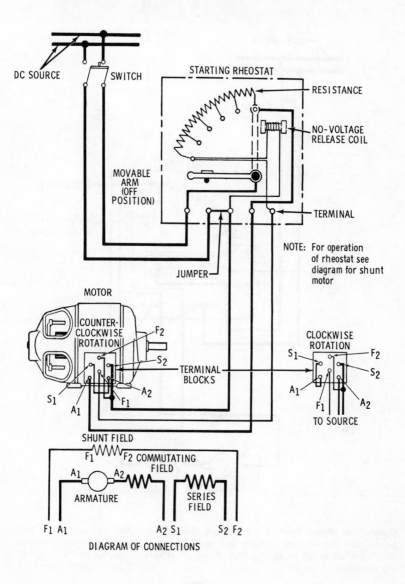

DC SOURCE

SWITCH

STARTING RHEOSTAT

RESISTANCE

NO-VOLTAGE
RELEASE COIL

MOVABLE
ARM
(OFF
POSITION)

TERMINAL

NOTE: For operation
of rheostat see
diagram for shunt
motor

JUMPER

MOTOR

COUNTER-
CLOCKWISE
ROTATION

F_2

S_2

S_1

A_1 F_1 A_2

TERMINAL
BLOCKS

CLOCKWISE
ROTATION

S_1 F_2

S_2

A_1

F_1 A_2

TO SOURCE

SHUNT FIELD

F_1 F_2 COMMUTATING
FIELD

A_1 A_2

ARMATURE

SERIES
FIELD

F_1 A_1 A_2 S_1 S_2 F_2

DIAGRAM OF CONNECTIONS

133

STARTING RHEOSTAT AND CONNECTION DIAGRAM
FOR DC SERIES-WOUND MOTOR

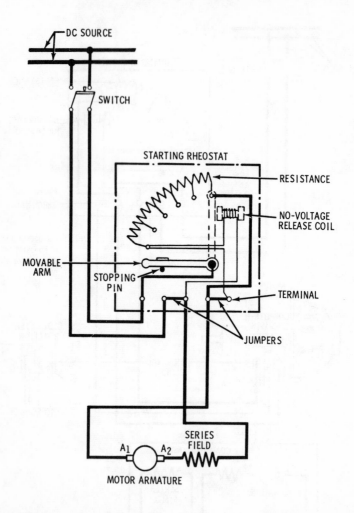

Operation—When field is interrupted due to an open connection or failure of source, the No Voltage release coil will automatically release the moveable arm, which by action of its spring (not shown in diagram) returns to its "Off" or starting position.

STARTING RHEOSTAT AND CONNECTION DIAGRAM
FOR DC SHUNT-WOUND MOTOR

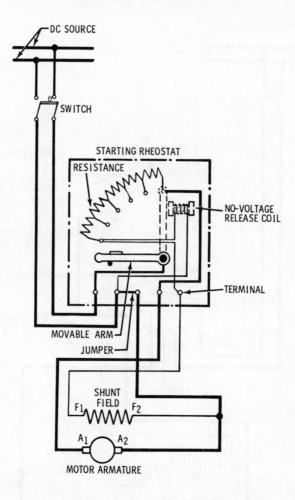

Operation—When voltage fails or shunt field is interrupted the No Voltage release coil will automatically release the moveable arm, which is returned to its starting position by action of holding spring (not shown in diagram). This method of starting will prevent accidental application of a heavy current through the motor armature, causing fuses to blow, or serious damage to motor.

STARTING RHEOSTAT AND CONNECTION DIAGRAM
FOR DC COMPOUND-WOUND MOTOR

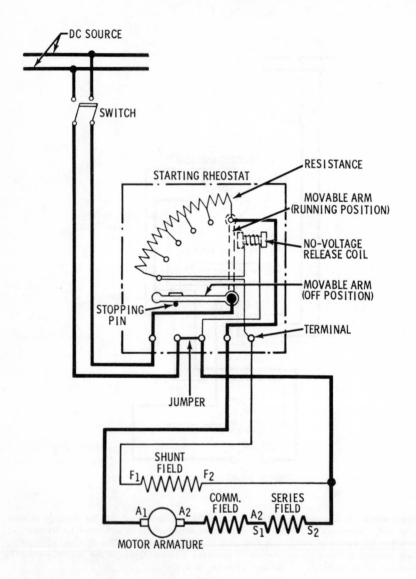

DC SOURCE

SWITCH

STARTING RHEOSTAT

RESISTANCE

MOVABLE ARM
(RUNNING POSITION)

NO-VOLTAGE
RELEASE COIL

MOVABLE ARM
(OFF POSITION)

STOPPING
PIN

TERMINAL

JUMPER

SHUNT
FIELD

F_1 F_2

COMM.
FIELD

SERIES
FIELD

A_1 A_2 A_2 S_1 S_2

MOTOR ARMATURE

CONNECTION DIAGRAMS
FOR DC SERIES-WOUND MOTORS

NONREVERSING COMMUTATING
POLE TYPE

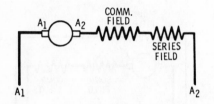

NONREVERSING NONCOMMUTATING
POLE TYPE

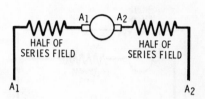

REVERSING COMMUTATING
POLE TYPE

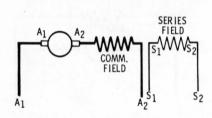

REVERSING NONCOMMUTATING
POLE TYPE

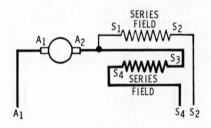

REVERSING NONCOMMUTATING
POLE TYPE

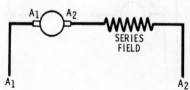

NONREVERSING NONCOMMUTATING
POLE TYPE

CONNECTION DIAGRAMS
FOR DC SHUNT-WOUND MOTORS

NONREVERSING COMMUTATING POLE TYPE

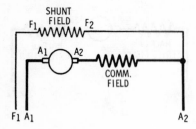

REVERSIBLE WITH COMMUTATING AND COMPENSATING FIELDS

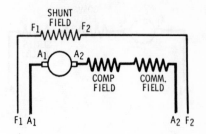

REVERSING COMMUTATING POLE TYPE

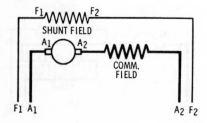

NONREVERSING NONCOMMUTATING POLE TYPE

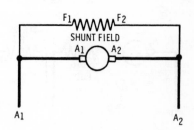

NONREVERSING NONCOMMUTATING POLE TYPE

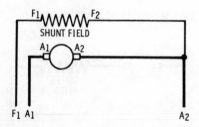

REVERSING NONCOMMUTATING POLE TYPE

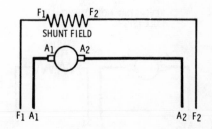

CONNECTION DIAGRAMS
FOR DC COMPOUND-WOUND MOTORS

NONREVERSING COMMUTATING
POLE TYPE

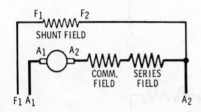

NONREVERSING NONCOMMUTATING
POLE TYPE

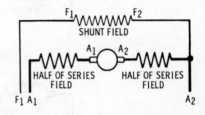

REVERSING COMMUTATING POLE TYPE

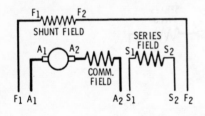

NONREVERSING NONCOMMUTATING
POLE TYPE

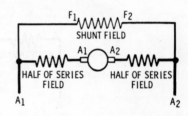

REVERSING NONCOMMUTATING
POLE TYPE

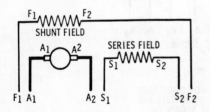

NONREVERSING NONCOMMUTATING
POLE TYPE

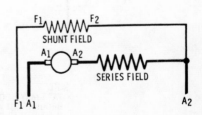

CONNECTION DIAGRAMS
FOR UNIVERSAL-TYPE MOTORS (AC OR DC)

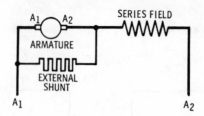

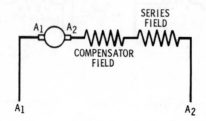

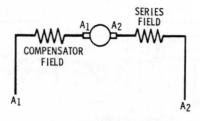

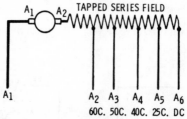

NOTE:
TAPS MAY BE OMITTED OR OTHER TAPS
BROUGHT OUT WHEN FREQUENCIES ARE
DIFFERENT FROM THOSE SHOWN.

CONNECTION DIAGRAMS
FOR DC GENERATORS (TWO-WIRE)

**SERIES GENERATOR WITHOUT
COMMUTATING POLES**

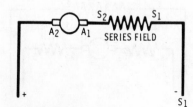

**SHUNT GENERATOR WITHOUT
COMMUTATING POLES**

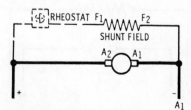

**SHUNT GENERATOR WITH
COMMUTATING POLES**

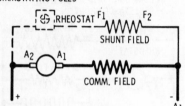

**SHUNT GENERATOR WITH COMMUTATING
AND COMPENSATING FIELDS**

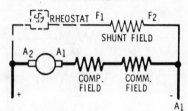

**COMPOUND GENERATOR WITHOUT
COMMUTATING POLES**

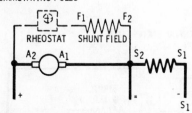

**COMPOUND GENERATOR WITH
COMMUTATING POLES**

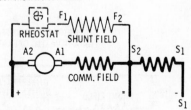

**COMPOUND GENERATOR WITH COMMUTATING
POLES AND COMPENSATING FIELD**

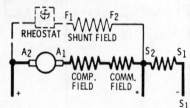

**SEPARATELY EXCITED GENERATOR WITH
COMMUTATING POLES**

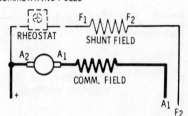

CONNECTION DIAGRAMS
FOR DC GENERATORS (TWO-WIRE)

SEPARATELY EXCITED GENERATOR

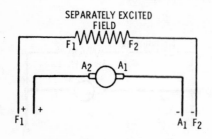

SEPARATELY EXCITED GENERATOR

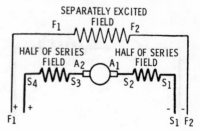

COMPOUND GENERATOR

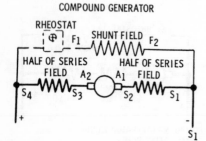

COMPOUND GENERATOR WITH
RESISTANCE SHUNT

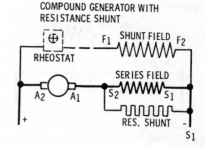

GENERATORS WITH DIFFERENTIAL SERIES FIELD
FOR AUTOMATIC OPERATION

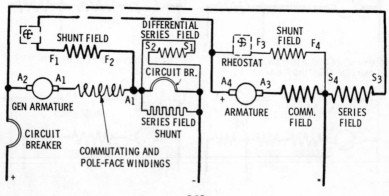

142

CONNECTION DIAGRAMS
FOR DC GENERATORS (THREE-WIRE)

SHUNT GENERATOR WITH COMMUTATING POLES

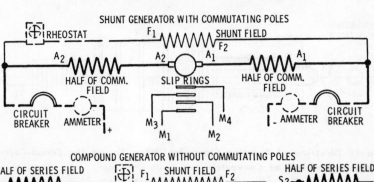

COMPOUND GENERATOR WITHOUT COMMUTATING POLES

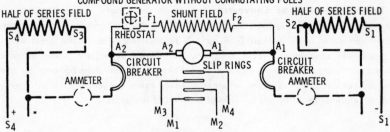

COMPOUND GENERATOR WITH COMMUTATING POLES

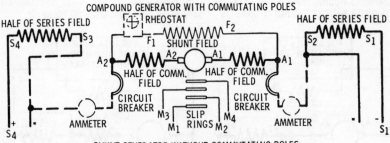

SHUNT GENERATOR WITHOUT COMMUTATING POLES

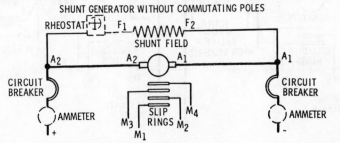

CONNECTION DIAGRAMS
FOR SYNCHRONOUS CONVERTERS (TWO-WIRE)

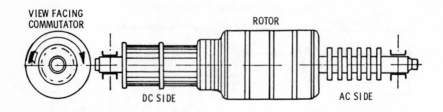

VIEW FACING
COMMUTATOR

ROTOR

DC SIDE

AC SIDE

Standard Direction of Rotation Clockwise When Facing the Direct-Current or Commutator End of Converter—This is obtained only if the terminal subnumerals 1, 2, 3 applied to the collector rings M_1, M_2, M_3 are connected to alternating-current generator leads marked T_1, T_2 and T_3 respectively. Due to the great variety of shunt-field connections, these diagrams are shown separately from the other connection diagrams. In some cases a shunt-field connection diagram may be used with only one machine diagram, whereas in other cases a machine diagram may be used in combination with any of several shunt-field diagrams.

COMPOUND-WOUND, THREE-PHASE, SYNCH.
CONVERTER WITHOUT COMMUTATING POLES

COMPOUND-WOUND, THREE-PHASE, SYNCHRONOUS
CONVERTER WITH COMMUTATING POLES

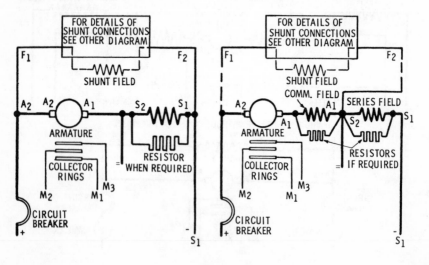

144

CONNECTION DIAGRAMS
FOR SYNCHRONOUS CONVERTERS (TWO-WIRE)

SHUNT-WOUND, THREE-PHASE, SYNCHRONOUS
CONVERTER WITHOUT COMMUTATING POLES

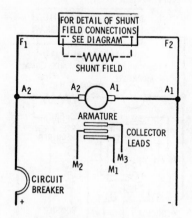

SHUNT-WOUND, THREE-PHASE, SYNCHRONOUS
CONVERTER WITH COMMUTATING POLES

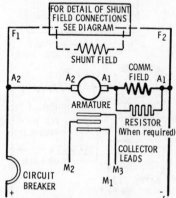

SHUNT-WOUND, SIX-PHASE, SYNCHRONOUS
CONVERTER WITHOUT COMMUTATING POLES

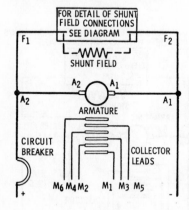

SHUNT-WOUND, SIX-PHASE, SYNCHRONOUS
CONVERTER WITH COMMUTATING POLES

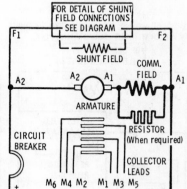

CONNECTION DIAGRAMS
FOR SYNCHRONOUS CONVERTERS (TWO-WIRE)

SHUNT-WOUND, SIX-PHASE, SYNCHRONOUS
CONVERTER WITH COMMUTATING FIELD,
AUXILIARY COMMUTATING FIELD AND
REVOLVING ARMATURE BOOSTER

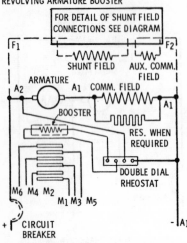

SHUNT-WOUND, SIX-PHASE, SYNCHRONOUS
CONVERTER WITH COMMUTATING FIELD,
AUXILIARY COMMUTATING FIELD AND
REVOLVING FIELD BOOSTER

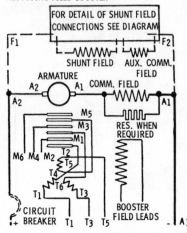

COMPOUND-WOUND, SIX-PHASE, SYNCHRONOUS
CONVERTER WITHOUT COMMUTATING POLES

COMPOUND-WOUND, SIX-PHASE, SYNCHRONOUS
CONVERTER WITH COMMUTATING POLES

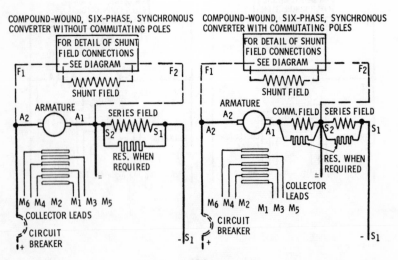

146

SHUNT-FIELD CONNECTIONS
FOR SYNCHRONOUS CONVERTERS

4-POLE, DOUBLE-THROW, BREAK-UP SWITCH

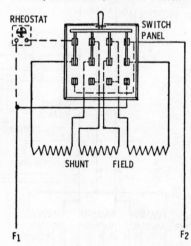

4-POLE, DOUBLE-THROW, BREAK-UP SWITCH WITH AUXILIARY COMMUTATING SHUNT FIELD

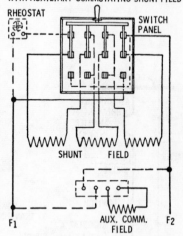

2-POLE, DOUBLE-THROW, DISCHARGE SWITCH FOR SEPARATE EXCITATION TO FIX POLARITY

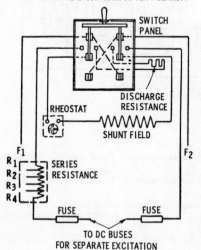

2-POLE, DOUBLE-THROW, DISCHARGE SWITCH FOR SELF EXCITATION

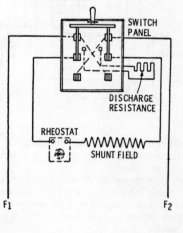

SYNCHRONOUS CONVERTER WIRING DIAGRAM

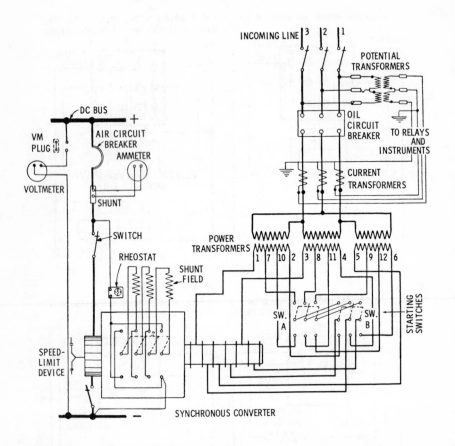

Synchronous Converter Starting.

The procedure in starting up a synchronous converter from the AC side is principally as follows:

(Step-1) With switch A and B thrown in upper position leads 1, 3, 5, 7, 8 and 9 connect the machine to its low voltage taps.

(Step-2) Now if switch A is thrown to its lower position (switch B remains unchanged) the machine will be connected to taps 1, 3, 5, 10, 11 and 12 which are the intermediate speed taps.

(Step-3) Finally, if switch A is opened and B is thrown in its lower position, the machine is connected to the full voltage or running speed terminals.

TRANSFORMER CONNECTIONS AND VECTOR DIAGRAMS
FOR SYNCHRONOUS CONVERTERS

CONNECTION FOR TRANSFORMATION
FROM DELTA TO Y

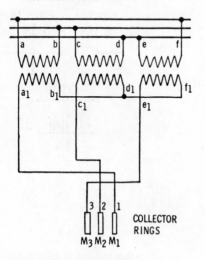

VECTOR DIAGRAM OF DELTA
TO Y CONNECTIONS

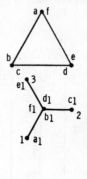

CONNECTION FOR TRANSFORMATION FROM
DELTA TO ZIG ZAG OR DISTRIBUTED - Y

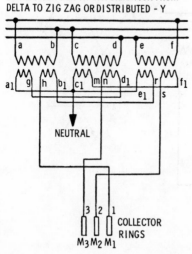

VECTOR DIAGRAM OF DELTA TO
DISTRIBUTED - Y CONNECTIONS

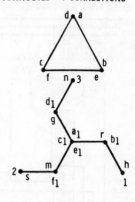

TRANSFORMER CONNECTIONS AND VECTOR DIAGRAMS
FOR SYNCHRONOUS CONVERTERS

DOUBLE-T CONNECTION FOR TRANSFORMATION
FROM TWO PHASE TO SIX PHASE

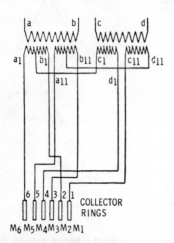

VECTOR DIAGRAM OF DOUBLE-T
CONNECTIONS

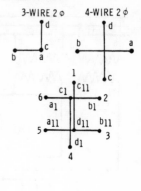

DIAMETRICAL CONNECTION FOR TRANSFORMATION
FROM 3 PHASE TO 6 PHASE

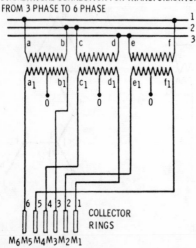

VECTOR DIAGRAM OF DIAMETRICAL
CONNECTIONS

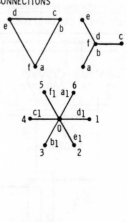

TRANSFORMER CONNECTIONS AND VECTOR DIAGRAMS
FOR SYNCHRONOUS CONVERTERS

CONNECTIONS FOR TRANSFORMATION
FROM DELTA TO DOUBLE DELTA

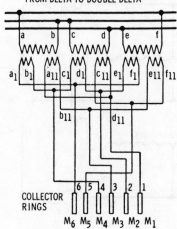

VECTOR DIAGRAM OF DELTA TO DOUBLE
DELTA CONNECTIONS

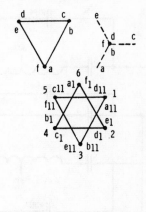

CONNECTIONS FOR TRANSFORMATION
FROM DELTA TO DOUBLE-Y

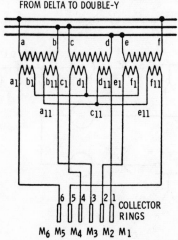

VECTOR DIAGRAM OF DELTA TO
DOUBLE-Y CONNECTIONS

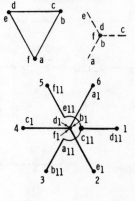

SQUIRREL-CAGE, INDUCTION-MOTOR STARTING

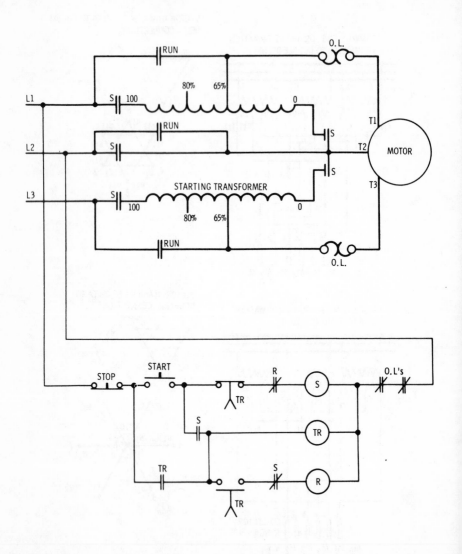

SQUIRREL-CAGE, INDUCTION-MOTOR STARTING

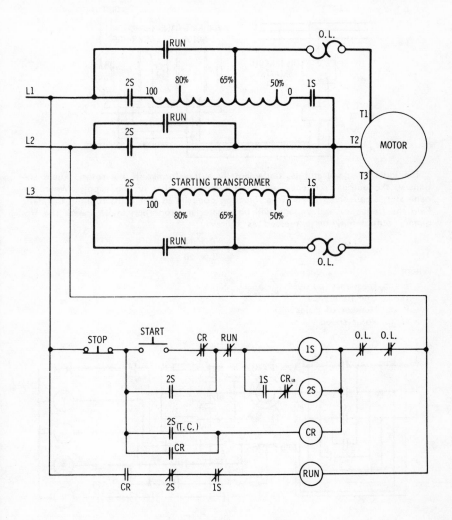

FREQUENCY-CONVERTER SET AND RESISTANCE STARTER FOR WOUND-ROTOR INDUCTION MOTOR

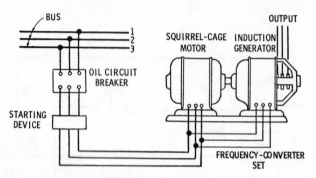

The induction generator is fundamentally a transformer. If the rotor is held stationary, the output frequency will be the same as that of the supply. When the generator is connected to run in a direction opposite to that of its rotating magnetic field the frequency and voltage will be greater in proportion to its speed. The frequency output may be expressed as follows:

$$f = f_L + \frac{P \times N}{2 \times 60}$$

Where

- f = Frequency output
- f_L = Line frequency
- P = Number of poles
- N = Rotor speed

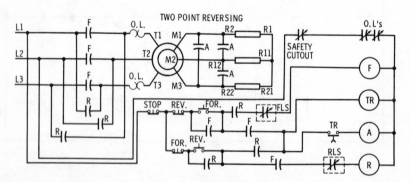

Starter for Wound-Rotor Induction Motor—The motor is started with the full amount of resistance in the rotor circuit. As the motor gains speed the rotor resistance is gradually cut out by decreasing the resistance.

FRACTIONAL-
HORSEPOWER
MOTOR
DIAGRAMS

FRACTIONAL-HORSEPOWER MOTORS

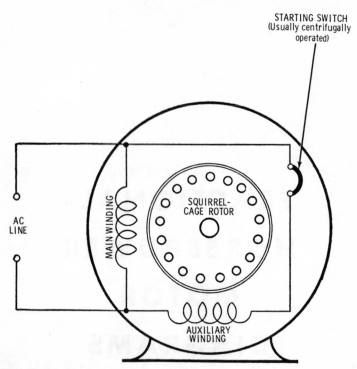

STARTING SWITCH
(Usually centrifugally operated)

AC LINE

MAIN WINDING

SQUIRREL-CAGE ROTOR

AUXILIARY WINDING

The Split-Phase Induction Motor—This motor type is commonly manufactured in fractional horsepower sizes. It is equipped with a squirrel-cage rotor for constant speed operation and has a starting winding of high resistance (commonly termed auxiliary winding), which is physically displaced in the stator from the main winding. This displacement produced by the relative electrical resistance values in the two windings, creates starting ability similar to that of a polyphase motor.

In series with the auxiliary winding is a starting switch (usually centrifugally operated) which opens the circuit when the motor has attained approximately 75 to 80 per cent of synchronous speed.

The function of the starting switch is to prevent the motor from drawing excessive current from the line and also to protect the starting winding from damage due to heating. The motor may be started in either direction by reversing either the main or auxiliary winding.

Single-phase, split-phase motors are suitable for oil burners, blowers, business machines, buffing machines, grinders, etc.

FRACTIONAL-HORSEPOWER MOTORS

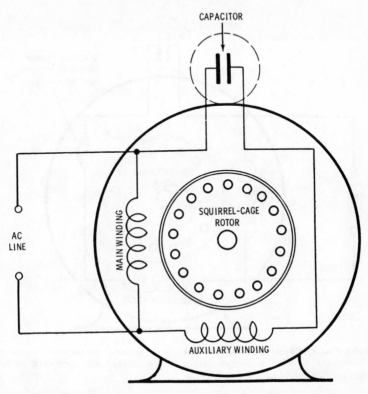

The Split-Phase, Permanently Connected Capacitor Motor—This type of split-phase motor, is commonly manufactured in fractional horsepower sizes.

In common with other types of split-phase motors, it is equipped with a squirrel-cage rotor and a main and auxiliary winding. A capacitor is permanently connected in series with the auxiliary winding, thus a motor of this type starts and runs with a fixed value of capacitance in series with the auxiliary winding.

The motor obtains its starting torque from a rotating magnetic field produced by the two stator windings physically displaced. The main winding is connected directly across the line, while the auxiliary or starting winding is connected to the line through the capacitor, giving an electrical phase displacement.

A motor of the permanent split-phase capacitor type is suitable for direct connected drives requiring low starting torque, such as fans, blowers, certain types of centrifugal pumps, etc.

FRACTIONAL-HORSEPOWER MOTORS

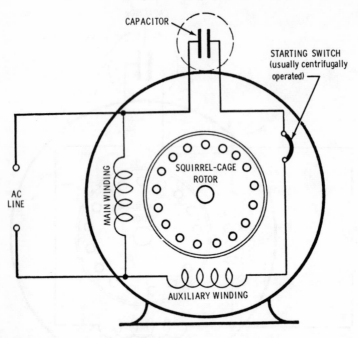

The Split-Phase, Capacitor-Start Motor—This fractional horsepower motor may be defined as a form of split-phase motor having a capacitor connected in series with the auxiliary winding.

The auxiliary circuit is opened by means of a centrifugally operated switch when the motor has attained a predetermined speed (usually approximately 70 to 80 per cent of synchronous speed).

A motor of this type is sometimes termed a capacitor-start, induction-run motor in contrast to the straight capacitor run type which is termed a capacitor-start, capacitor-run motor.

The rotor is of the squirrel cage type as in other split-phase motors. The main winding is connected directly across the line, while the auxiliary or starting winding is connected through a capacitor which may be connected into the circuit through a transformer with suitable designed windings and capacitor of such values that the two windings will be approximately 90 degrees apart.

This type of motor is particularly suited for such applications as air conditioning, domestic and commercial refrigeration, belt driven fans, etc.

FRACTIONAL-HORSEPOWER MOTORS

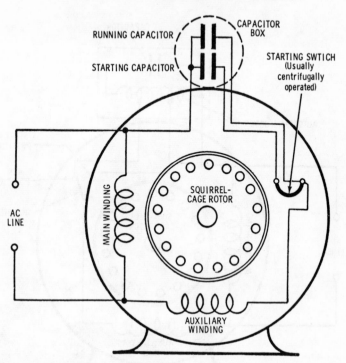

The Split-Phase, Capacitor-Run Motor—This type of motor, also termed two-value capacitor-motor has a running capacitor permanently connected in series with the auxiliary winding, the starting capacitor being in parallel with the running capacitor only during the starting period.

In operation the motor starts with the starting switch closed. After the motor has attained a speed of approximately 70 to 80 per cent of synchronous, the starting switch opens, thus disconnecting the starting capacitor.

The running capacitor is usually of the paper-spaced oil filled type, normally rated at 330 volt AC for continuous operation. They usually range from 3 to 16 microfarads, depending upon the size of the motor.

The starting capacitor is generally of the electrolytic type and may range in sizes of from 80 to 300 microfarads approximately, for 110 volt, 60 cycle motors.

This type of motor is designed for applications requiring high starting torque, such as compressors, loaded conveyors, reciprocating pumps, refrigeration compressors, stokers, etc.

FRACTIONAL-HORSEPOWER MOTORS

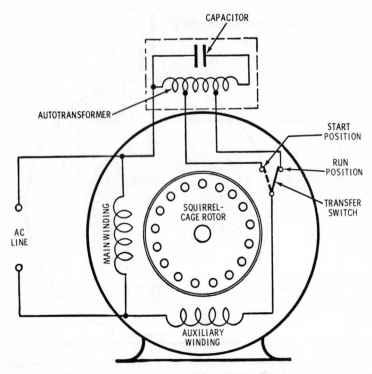

The Split-Phase, Capacitor-Run Motor—Another type of two-value capacitor motor uses a capacitor transformer unit. The motor is of the split-phase squirrel cage type with the main and auxiliary winding physically displaced in the stator.

This type of motor employs a **transfer switch** which is equivalent to a single-pole, double-throw switch, by means of which a high voltage is impressed across the capacitor during the starting period.

After the motor has attained a speed of 70 to 80 per cent of synchronous ,the transfer switch operates to change the voltage taps on the transformer. The voltage impressed upon the capacitor by means of the transformer will be of a value of from 600 to 800 volts during the starting period and approximately 350 volts for continuous operation.

This type of motor is designed for applications requiring high starting torque such as compressors, loaded conveyors, reciprocating pumps, refrigeration compressors, stokers, etc.

FRACTIONAL-HORSEPOWER MOTORS

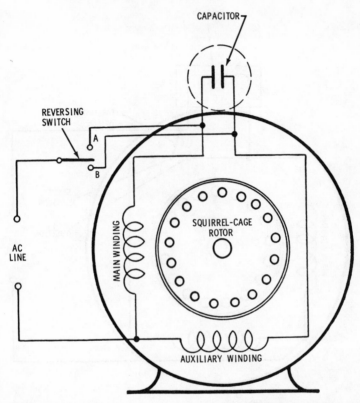

CAPACITOR

REVERSING
SWITCH

A
B

AC
LINE

MAIN WINDING

SQUIRREL-CAGE
ROTOR

AUXILIARY WINDING

The Split-Phase, Capacitor-Run, Induction Motor (Reversible Type)—In applications where it is necessary to employ a reversible high-torque intermittently rated
capacitor type, a motor connected as shown has found employment.

When the reversing switch is in the **B** position, the auxiliary winding becomes
the main winding, and the main winding becomes the auxiliary winding. With
the switch in the **A** position, both windings function as shown in the diagram.

Since the direction of rotation in split-phase motors is always from the auxiliary
winding toward the main winding, it follows that an interchange of the windings
will also reverse the direction of rotation.

From the foregoing it follows that with motor connections arranged in this
manner, the main and auxiliary windings in the motor must be identical, both as to
size of wire and number of effective turns.

FRACTIONAL-HORSEPOWER MOTORS

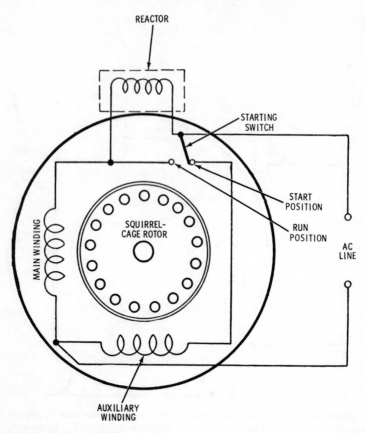

REACTOR

STARTING
SWITCH

START
POSITION

RUN
POSITION

AC
LINE

MAIN WINDING

SQUIRREL-
CAGE ROTOR

AUXILIARY
WINDING

The Reactor-Start, Split-Phase, Induction Motor—This type, in common with other types of split-phase motors, is equipped with an auxiliary winding, displaced in magnetic position from, and connected in parallel with the main winding.

The function of the reactor is to reduce the starting current and increase the current lag in the main winding. At approximately 75 per cent of synchronous speed the starting switch operates to shunt out the reactor, disconnecting the auxiliary winding from the circuit.

The starting switch must be of such construction so as to be equal to a single-pole, double-throw switch.

This is a constant speed motor and lends itself best for such applications as light running machines such as fans, small blowers, business machines, grinders, etc.

FRACTIONAL-HORSEPOWER MOTORS

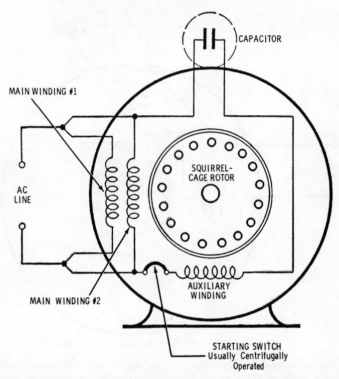

CAPACITOR

MAIN WINDING #1

AC
LINE

SQUIRREL-
CAGE ROTOR

MAIN WINDING #2

AUXILIARY
WINDING

STARTING SWITCH
Usually Centrifugally
Operated

The Split-Phase, Single-Value Capacitor Motor (Dual-Voltage Type)—A motor of this type differs from the conventional type of capacitor motor in that it has two identical main windings arranged for either series or parallel connections.

With the main windings connected in parallel the line voltage is usually 115 volts, whereas when the main windings are connected in series a line voltage of 230 volts is usually employed.

The starting switch and operating characteristics of the motor do not differ from single-value capacitor-start motors previously described.

In common with other types of split-phase motors, the auxiliary winding is a separate winding displaced in space from the main winding 90 degrees. Also in series with the auxiliary winding is the usual centrifugal switch and starting capacitor.

A winding arrangement of this type gives only half as much starting torque on 115 volts as on a 230 volt winding.

FRACTIONAL-HORSEPOWER MOTORS

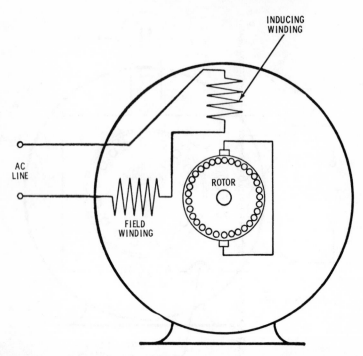

The Repulsion Motor—By definition, a repulsion motor is a single-phase motor which has a stator winding arranged for connection to the source of power and a rotor winding connected to a commutator. Brushes and commutators are short-circuited and are so placed that the magnetic axis of the rotor winding is inclined to the magnetic axis of the stator winding.

It has a varying speed characteristic, a high starting torque and moderate starting current.

Due to its low power factor except at high speeds, it is often modified into the **compensated repulsion motor,** which has another set of brushes placed midway between the short-circuited set. This added set is connected in series with the stator winding.

The Repulsion-Start Induction Motor—By definition, a repulsion-start induction motor is a single-phase motor having the same windings as a repulsion motor, but at a predetermined speed the rotor winding is short-circuited or otherwise connected to give the equivalent of a squirrel-cage winding. This type of motor starts as a repulsion motor, but operates as an induction motor with constant-speed characteristics.

FRACTIONAL-HORSEPOWER MOTORS

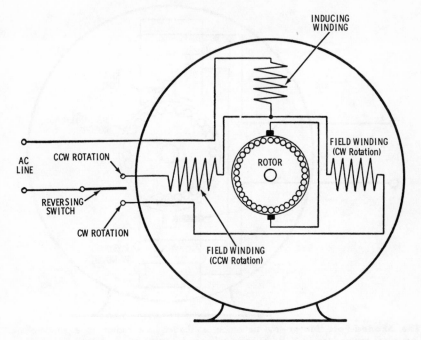

The Repulsion-Start Induction Motor (Reversible Type)—In certain applications, it is necessary to reverse the direction of rotation. A motor of this type has two stator windings displaced as indicated. Reversal of the motor can be accomplished by interchanging the field winding connections.

Thus, for example, with the switch in the upper position, the motor will rotate in a counter-clockwise direction, whereas if the switch is in the lower position the motor will run in the opposite direction, or clock-wise.

The current induced in the armature is carried by the brushes and commutator, resulting in high starting torque. When nearly synchronous speed is attained the commutator is short-circuited so that the armature is then similar in its functions to a squirrel-cage armature.

FRACTIONAL-HORSEPOWER MOTORS

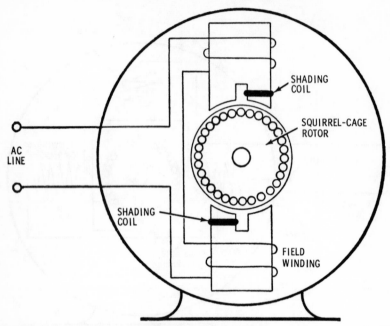

The Shaded-Pole Motor—By definition a shaded-pole motor is a single-phase induction motor provided with an auxiliary short-circuited winding or windings displaced in magnetic position from the main winding.

Although there are a number of different construction methods employed, principally the motor operates as follows: The shading coil (from which the motor has derived its name) consists of low resistance copper links embedded in one side of each stator pole, and are used to provide the necessary starting torque. When the current increases in the main coils a current is induced in the shading coils that opposes the magnetic field building up in part of the pole pieces they surround.

When the main coil current decreases, that in the shading coil also decreases, until the pole pieces are uniformly magnetized. As the main coil current and the pole piece magnetic flux continue to decrease, current in the shading coils reverses and tends to maintain the flux in part of the pole pieces.

When the main coil current drops to zero, current still flows in the shading coils to give the magnetic effect which causes the coils to produce a rotating magnetic field which makes the motor self starting.

This motor is used largely where the power requirements are small, such as in electric clocks, instruments, toys, hair dryers, small fans, etc. It is simple in construction and low in cost and is in addition very rugged and reliable.

FRACTIONAL-HORSEPOWER MOTORS

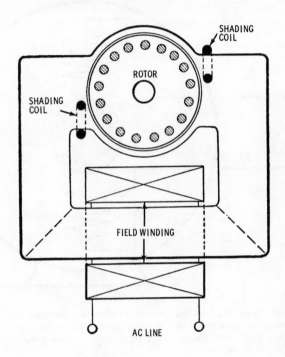

The Shaded-Pole Motor (Skeleton Type)—This type of motor is built for applications where the power requirements are very small. The field circuit with its winding, is built around the conventional squirrel-cage rotor and consists of punchings that are stacked alternately to form overlapping joints, in the same manner that small transformer cores are assembled.

Motors of this class will operate only on alternating current; they are simple in construction, low in cost and extremely rugged and reliable. Their principal limitations are, however, low efficiency and a low starting and running torque.

A shaded-pole motor is not reversible, unless shading coils are provided on each side of the pole, and means for opening one and closing the other coil are provided.

The inherently high slip of a shaded-pole motor makes it convenient to obtain speed variation on a fan load, for example, by reducing the impressed voltage.

FRACTIONAL-HORSEPOWER MOTORS

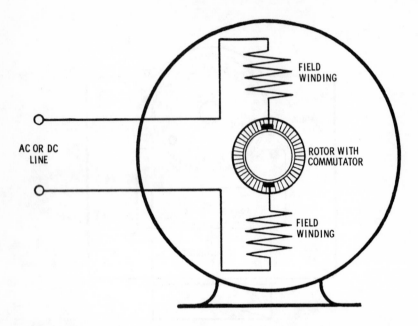

The Universal Type Motor—The universal motor is designed for operation on either alternating or direct current. It is of the series-wound type, that is, it is provided with a field winding on the stator which is connected in series with a commutating winding on the rotor.

Universal motors are commonly manufactured in fractional horsepower sizes and are preferred because of their use on either AC or DC currents, particularly in areas where power companies supply both types of current.

Full-load speeds generally range from 5,000 to 10,000 r.p.m. with no-load speeds from 12,000 to 18,000 r.p.m. Typical applications are portable tools, office appliances, electric cleaners, kitchen appliances, sewing machines, etc.

The speed of universal motors can be adjusted by connecting a resistance of proper value in series with the motor. Advantages of this speed control method is obvious, in such applications as motor operated sewing machines, where it is necessary to operate the motor over a wide range of speed.

In such applications adjustable resistances are used and the speed varied at will of the operator. Universal motors may be either compensated or uncompensated, the latter type being used for the higher speeds and lower ratings only.

SYNCHRONISM INDICATOR AND WIRING DIAGRAMS

GENERAL METHOD OF SYNCHRONIZING

Parallel Operation of Synchronous Generators.

Before generator #2 can be connected in parallel with generator #1, the following conditions must be obtained:

(1) Both machines must have the same frequency and waveform.
(2) Their terminal voltages must be equal.
(3) Their sequence of maximum potential values must be the same.
When synchronizing proceed as follows:

I. Lamp Synchronizing—Machine #1 is running and supplying the load. Its oil circuit breaker is closed and the running plug is inserted. Bring machine #2 up to voltage by slowly increasing the speed of its prime mover. As the speed of machine #2 increases, insert the starting plug; when the machines are running at nearly the same speed, the synchronizing lamps light up then go out, light up again, etc. If the machines are in step with lamps out or lamps in, (depending on whether light or dark lamp connections are used) wait until they go out for a few seconds then close the oil circuit breaker on machine #2 and the machines are now in parallel.

II. Indicator Synchronizing—Proceed same as before: The rotary motion of the pointer on the indicator indicates whether the generator to be synchronized is running too slow or too fast. When the pointer remains stationary in the vertical position, the two machines are in synchronism and the oil circuit breaker can be closed.

After paralleling the two machines, adjust the mechanical power input and the generated emf until each machine supplies its share of the total load, and the power factor of each machine is the same and equal to that of the total load.

METHOD OF SYNCHRONIZING 2 AC GENERATORS

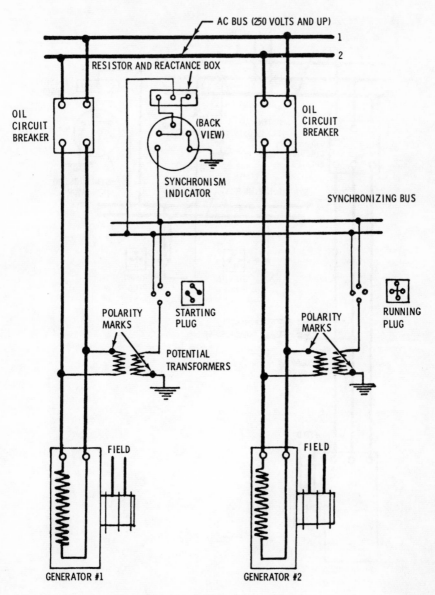

AC BUS (250 VOLTS AND UP)

1

2

RESISTOR AND REACTANCE BOX

OIL
CIRCUIT
BREAKER

(BACK
VIEW)

SYNCHRONISM
INDICATOR

OIL
CIRCUIT
BREAKER

SYNCHRONIZING BUS

POLARITY
MARKS

STARTING
PLUG

POLARITY
MARKS

RUNNING
PLUG

POTENTIAL
TRANSFORMERS

FIELD

FIELD

GENERATOR #1

GENERATOR #2

171

METHOD OF SYNCHRONIZING BUS AND MACHINE

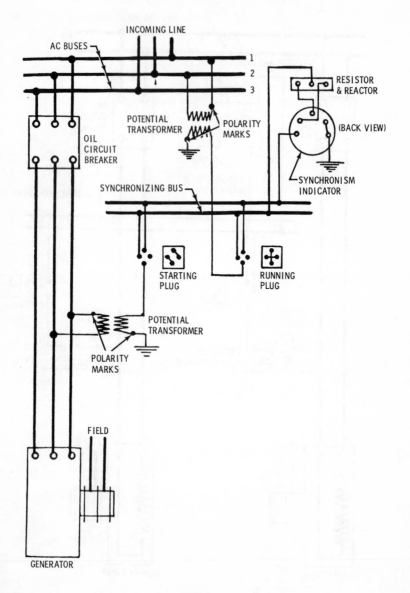

SYNCHRONIZING CONNECTION ACROSS A DELTA
DIAMETRICAL BANK OF TRANSFORMERS

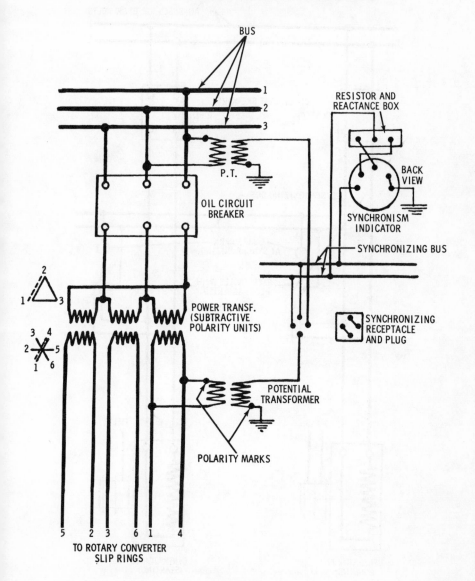

BUS

RESISTOR AND
REACTANCE BOX

P.T.

OIL CIRCUIT
BREAKER

BACK
VIEW

SYNCHRONISM
INDICATOR

SYNCHRONIZING BUS

POWER TRANSF.
(SUBTRACTIVE
POLARITY UNITS)

SYNCHRONIZING
RECEPTACLE
AND PLUG

POTENTIAL
TRANSFORMER

POLARITY MARKS

TO ROTARY CONVERTER
SLIP RINGS

METHOD OF SYNCHRONIZING (LAMPS DARK)

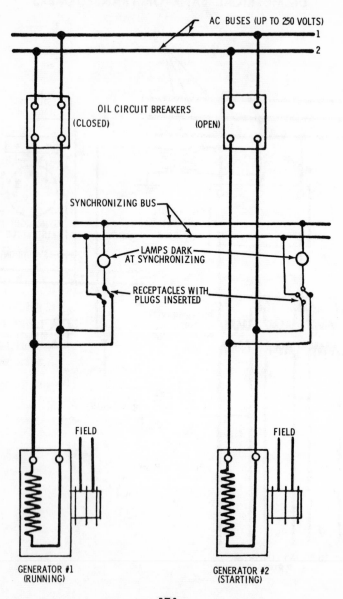

AC BUSES (UP TO 250 VOLTS)

1

2

OIL CIRCUIT BREAKERS

(CLOSED)

(OPEN)

SYNCHRONIZING BUS

LAMPS DARK
AT SYNCHRONIZING

RECEPTACLES WITH
PLUGS INSERTED

FIELD

FIELD

GENERATOR #1
(RUNNING)

GENERATOR #2
(STARTING)

METHOD OF SYNCHRONIZING (LAMPS BRIGHT)

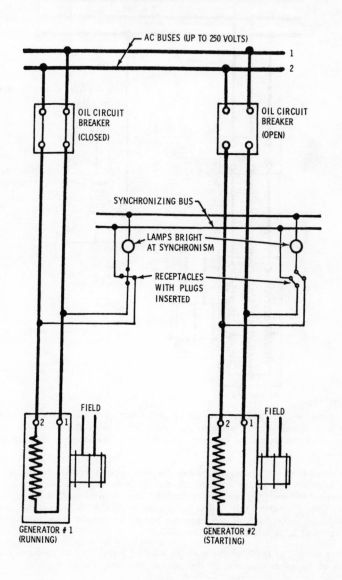

PHASE-ROTATION TEST

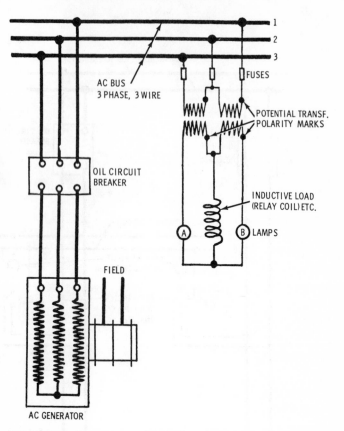

Before two AC generators can be synchronized, it is necessary, in addition to having one phase of the machine in synchronism with the phase of the other machine, that the sequence of maximum potential values in various phases shall be the same.

Adjustments of the phases to obtain this sequence is known as "phase rotation test." To obtain the phase rotation of the machine, proceed as follows: Connect two lamps "A" and "B" and an inductive load as shown. One lamp will glow brighter than the other; and if that lamp should be the "B" lamp, the phase relation is clockwise or 1-2-3. If on the other hand "A" should glow the brighter, the phase rotation is counterclockwise or 3-2-1.

After a check, the leads of the machine may be transposed to conform with phase rotation of the other machine, or the bus, as the case may be.

TRANSFORMER CONNECTIONS

CIRCUIT CONNECTIONS AND DEFINITIONS OF
VOLTAGE AND CURRENT IN THREE-PHASE SYSTEMS

In a three-phase system, (transformer-circuit or apparatus) there are two voltages between which a sharp distinction must be made: The voltage between the phase conductors, and the voltage from phase conductor to neutral (or ground where the neutral is at ground potential).

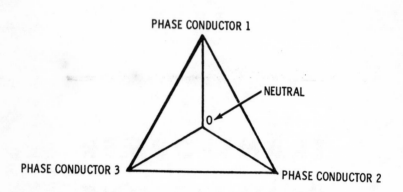

In the usual diagrammatic representation as above, these voltages are denoted as the delta voltage and the star voltage.

If then, 1, 2 and 3 are the three-phase conductors of a three-phase circuit, and 0 is the neutral (regardless of whether it actually exists as conductor or not), the delta voltages 1-2, 2-3, 3-1 are variously called the, Line Voltage, Voltage Between Lines, Voltage Between Conductors, or simply the Three-Phase Voltage or the voltage of the system; The star voltages 0-1, 0-2, 0-3 are similarly called the Voltage To Ground, Voltage To Neutral, or Neutral Voltage, etc.

CIRCUIT CONNECTIONS AND DEFINITIONS OF VOLTAGE AND CURRENT IN THREE-PHASE SYSTEMS
—continued

delta voltage = 1.73 times star voltage.

$$\text{star voltage} = \frac{\text{delta voltage}}{1.73}$$

Thus the delta voltage is the higher, the star voltage being only a part of the delta voltage.

Similarly a distinction is made between the delta current and the star current in a three-phase system. The delta current is the current which flows from phase to phase: from 1 to 2, from 2 to 3, from 3 to 1.

The star current is often simply denoted as the Current or Current Per Phase. Line Current is the current flowing in the phase conductors in 1, or 2, or 3 and may be supposed to flow towards the neutral 0.

star current = 1.73 times delta current

$$\text{delta current} = \frac{\text{star current}}{1.73}$$

When speaking of the voltage and the current or line voltage and line current of a three-phase system, without further qualifications, the delta voltage and the star current are understood.

In the conventional denotations, voltage and current in the three-phase system thus do not correspond to each other; and therefore are not in phase with each other on noninductive load, but show a phase displacement of 30 degrees, the angle 0-1-2 above.

Transformers and Connections.

A transformer is defined as a form of stationary induction apparatus in which the primary and secondary windings are ordinarily insulated one from another. A transformer does not generate power but merely changes the power from one voltage to another.

CIRCUIT CONNECTIONS AND DEFINITIONS OF VOLTAGE AND CURRENT IN THREE-PHASE SYSTEMS
—continued

The three-phase transformer consists of three primary and three secondary windings (see A below) usually connected in star or delta respectively.

Single-phase transformers (see B below) connected in star or delta are often preferable to three-phase transformers because single-phase reverse units are less expensive also because damage to one single-phase transformer may be repaired, while another identical spare transformer is interconnected in the three-phase unit without loss of service.

When two sets of transformers are connected in parallel to the primary and secondary circuits of a three-phase system, any combination of delta and star may be used in each set except that, with one set of transformers connected in delta-star or star-delta, the other set may not be connected delta-delta or star-star.

For examples of transformer connections, see the following pages.

A

B

Three-phase transformer

Single-phase transformer

TRANSFORMER CONNECTIONS

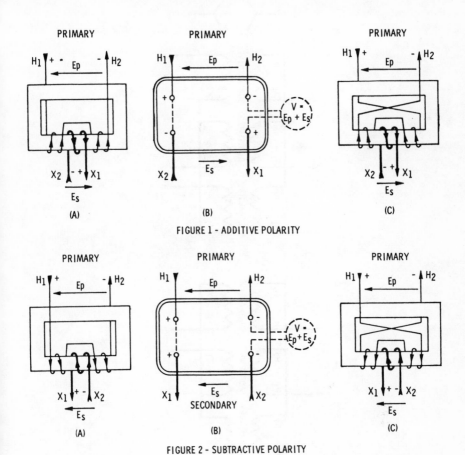

FIGURE 1 - ADDITIVE POLARITY

FIGURE 2 - SUBTRACTIVE POLARITY

To test for polarity: with primary and secondary in series (one primary lead being connected to the adjacent secondary lead) the transformer is excited from an AC source on either side and the voltages across the high-voltage winding and between the free primary and secondary terminals are measured. If the latter voltage is found to be less than that across the high-voltage winding, the polarity is subtractive, if more it is additive. In testing for polarity a fraction of the rated voltage is sufficient.

TRANSFORMER CONNECTIONS

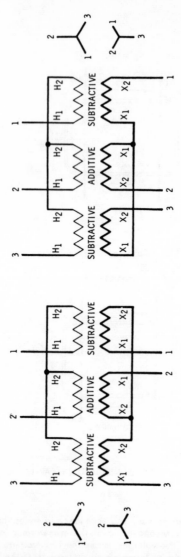

Connections for Star-Star Power Transformer Group to Obtain Additive or Subtractive Line Polarity.

TRANSFORMER CONNECTIONS

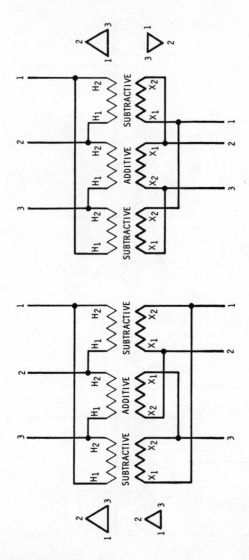

Connections for Delta-Delta Power Transformer Group to Obtain Additive or Subtractive Line Polarity.

TRANSFORMER CONNECTIONS

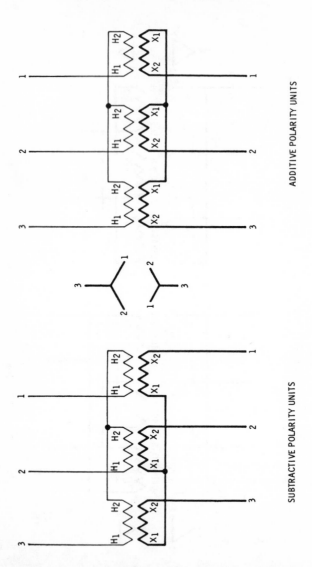

ADDITIVE POLARITY UNITS

SUBTRACTIVE POLARITY UNITS

Connections for Obtaining Additive Line Polarity with Transformer Units of Either Additive or Subtractive Polarity in Star-Star Groups.

TRANSFORMER CONNECTIONS

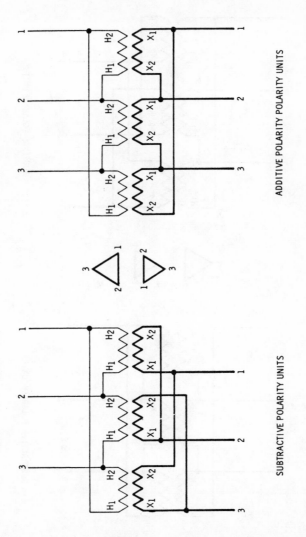

ADDITIVE POLARITY POLARITY UNITS

SUBTRACTIVE POLARITY UNITS

Connections for Obtaining Additive Line Polarity with Transformer Units of Either Additive or Subtractive Polarity in Delta-Delta Groups.

TRANSFORMER CONNECTIONS

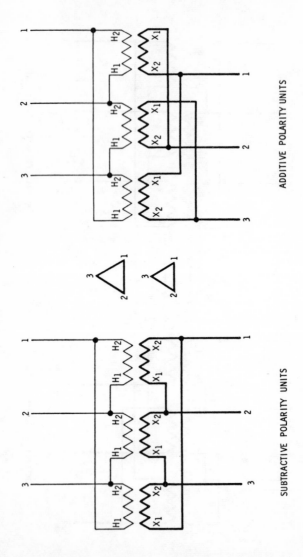

ADDITIVE POLARITY UNITS

SUBTRACTIVE POLARITY UNITS

Connections for Obtaining Subtractive Line Polarity with Transformer Units of Either Additive or Subtractive Polarity in Delta-Delta Groups.

TRANSFORMER CONNECTIONS

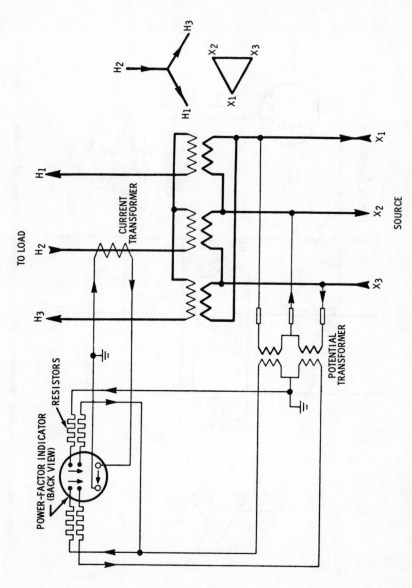

Connections for Typical Power Factor Indicator Across a Star-Delta Transformer Bank.

TRANSFORMER CONNECTIONS

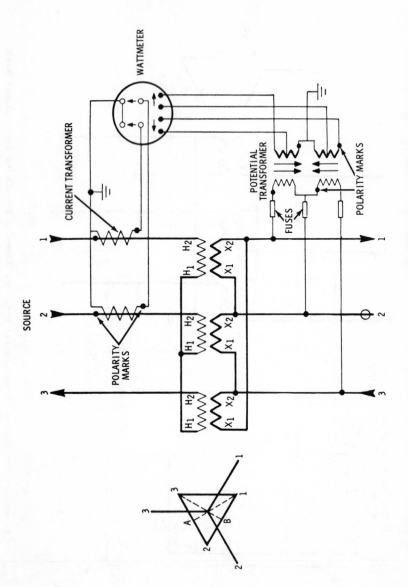

Connections for Indicating Wattmeter Across a Star-Delta Group of Power Transformers.

TRANSFORMER CONNECTIONS

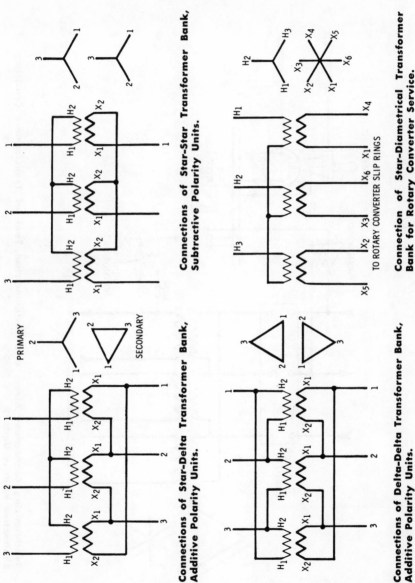

Connections of Star-Star Transformer Bank, Subtractive Polarity Units.

Connections of Star-Delta Transformer Bank, Additive Polarity Units.

Connection of Star-Diametrical Transformer Bank for Rotary Converter Service.

Connections of Delta-Delta Transformer Bank, Additive Polarity Units.

189

TRANSFORMER CONNECTIONS

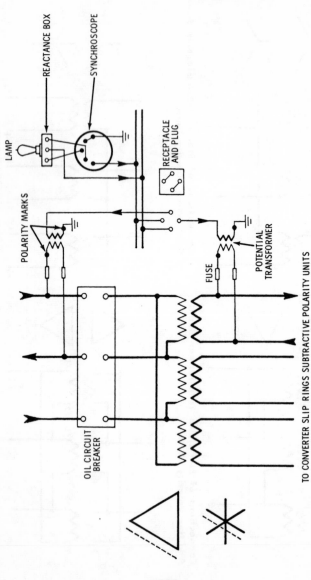

LAMP

REACTANCE BOX

SYNCHROSCOPE

RECEPTACLE AND PLUG

POLARITY MARKS

FUSE

POTENTIAL TRANSFORMER

OIL CIRCUIT BREAKER

TO CONVERTER SLIP RINGS SUBTRACTIVE POLARITY UNITS

Synchronizing Connections Across a Delta–Diametrical Bank of Transformers Consisting of Subtractive Polarity Units.

TRANSFORMER CONNECTIONS

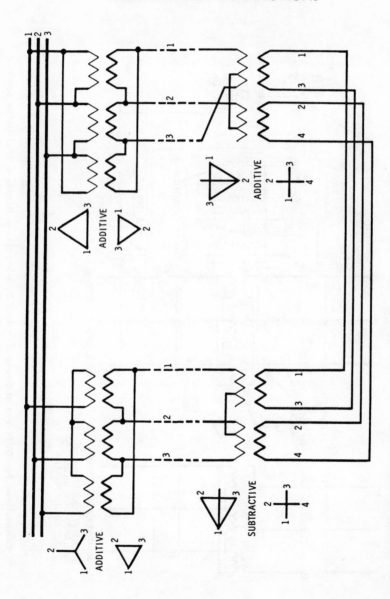

Three-Phase Voltages Carried Across Various Transformer Group Forms Resulting in In-Phase Voltages on the Quarter-Phase System.

TRANSFORMER CONNECTIONS

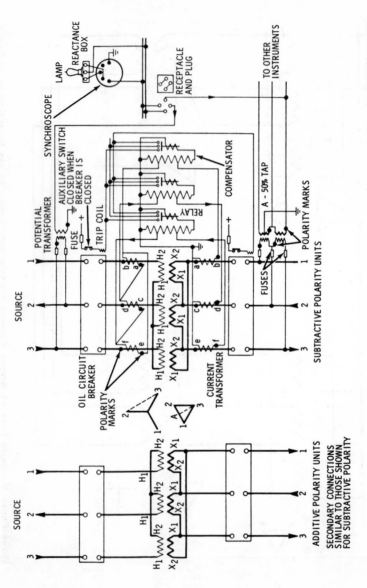

Connections for Differential Protection and Synchronizing Across a Star-Delta Bank.

TRANSFORMER CONNECTIONS

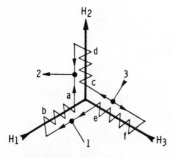

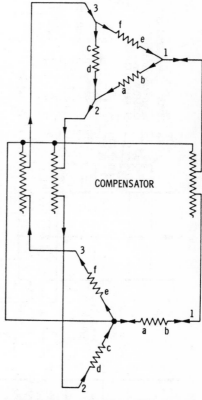

PHASE POSITION AND DIRECTION OF CURRENTS IN SECONDARIES ON HIGH-VOLTAGE SIDE (8.66 AMPERES)

PRIMARIES AND SECONDARIES OF CURRENT TRANSFORMERS ON HIGH-VOLTAGE SIDE

COMPENSATOR

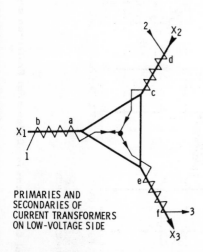

PRIMARIES AND SECONDARIES OF CURRENT TRANSFORMERS ON LOW-VOLTAGE SIDE

PHASE POSITION AND DIRECTION OF CURRENTS IN SECONDARIES ON LOW-VOLTAGE SIDE (5.00 AMPERES)

Vector Diagram Representing Current Relations at a Given Instant in Current Transformers Arranged for Differential Protection with Power Transformers Connected in Star-Delta.

TRANSFORMER CONNECTIONS

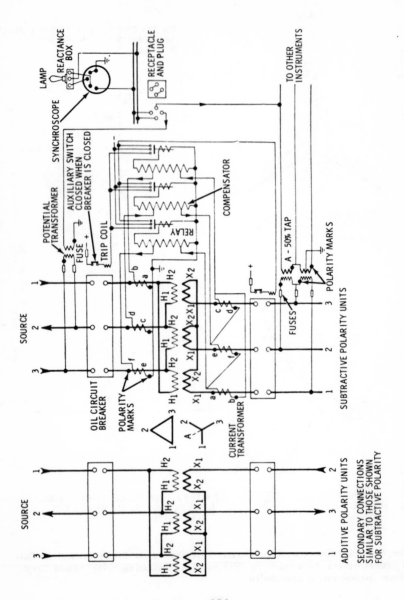

Typical Connections for Differential Protection and Synchronizing Across a Delta-Star Bank.

TRANSFORMER CONNECTIONS

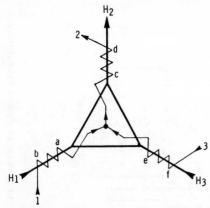

PRIMARIES AND SECONDARIES OF CURRENT
TRANSFORMERS ON HIGH-VOLTAGE SIDE.

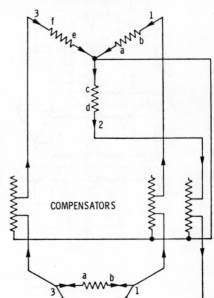

PHASE POSITION AND
DIRECTION OF CURRENTS
IN SECONDARIES ON
HIGH-VOLTAGE SIDE.
(5.00 AMPERES)

COMPENSATORS

PHASE POSITION AND DIRECTION OF CURRENTS
IN SECONDARIES ON LOW-VOLTAGE SIDE.
(8.66 AMPERES)

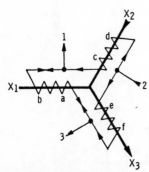

PRIMARIES AND SECONDARIES OF
CURRENT TRANSFORMERS ON LOW-
VOLTAGE SIDE.

Vector Diagram Representing Current Relations at a Given Instant in Current Transformers Arranged for Differential Protection with Power Transformers Connected in Delta-Star.

TRANSFORMER CONNECTIONS

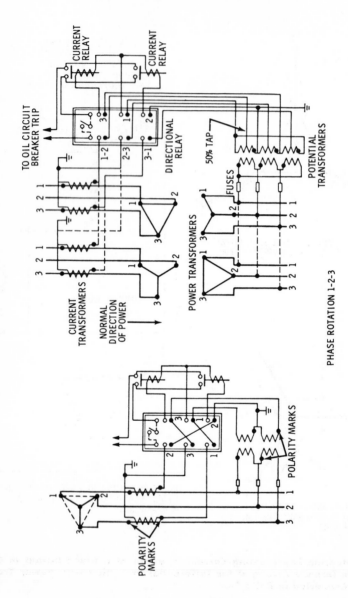

Differential Relay Connected Across a Star-Delta or Delta-Star Group of Power Transformers.

196

TRANSFORMER CONNECTIONS

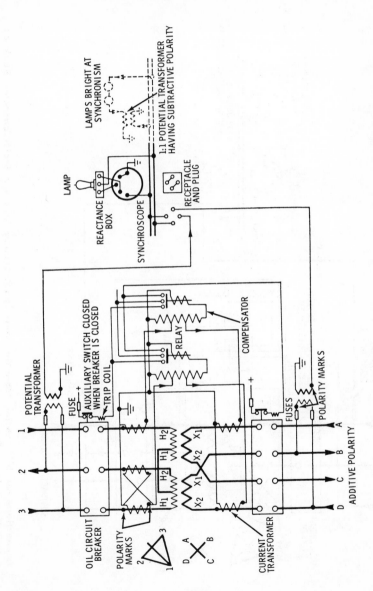

Connections for Differential Protection and Synchronizing Across a Scott-Connected Bank of Additive Polarity Transformers.

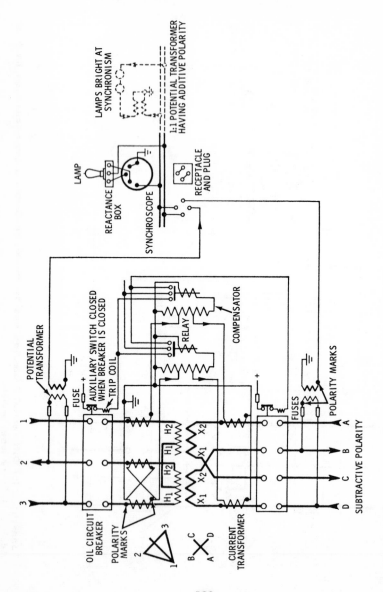

Connections for Differential Protection and Synchronizing Across a Scott-Connected Bank of Subtractive Polarity Transformers.

TRANSFORMER CONNECTIONS

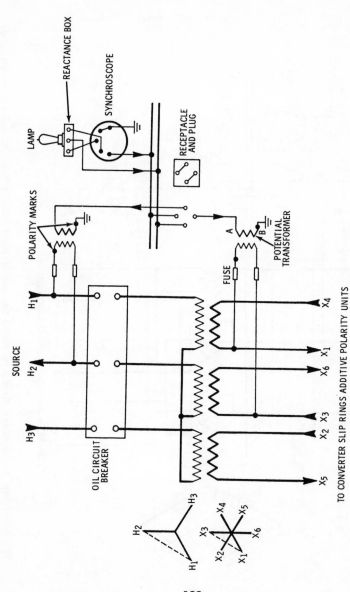

Synchronizing Connections Across a Star-Diametrical Bank of Transformers Consisting of Additive Polarity Units.

TRANSFORMER CONNECTIONS

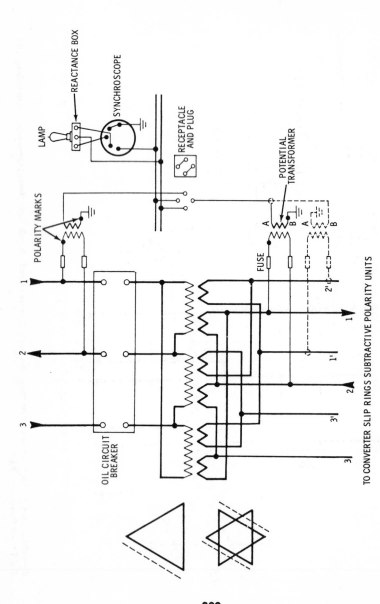

TO CONVERTER SLIP RINGS SUBTRACTIVE POLARITY UNITS

Synchronizing Connections Across a Delta-Double Delta Bank of Transformers Consisting of Subtractive Polarity Units.

TRANSFORMER CONNECTIONS

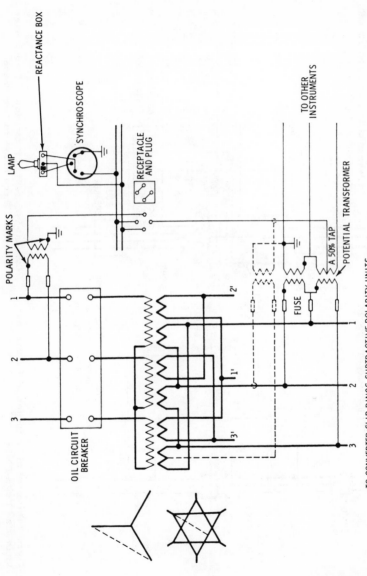

REACTANCE BOX

SYNCHROSCOPE

LAMP

POLARITY MARKS

RECEPTACLE
AND PLUG

TO OTHER
INSTRUMENTS

POTENTIAL TRANSFORMER

A 50% TAP

FUSE

1

2

3

2'

1'

3'

OIL CIRCUIT
BREAKER

TO CONVERTER SLIP RINGS SUBTRACTIVE POLARITY UNITS

Synchronizing Connections Across a Star-Double Delta Bank of Transformers Consisting of Subtractive Polarity Units.

201

CURRENT-DIFFERENTIAL PROTECTION

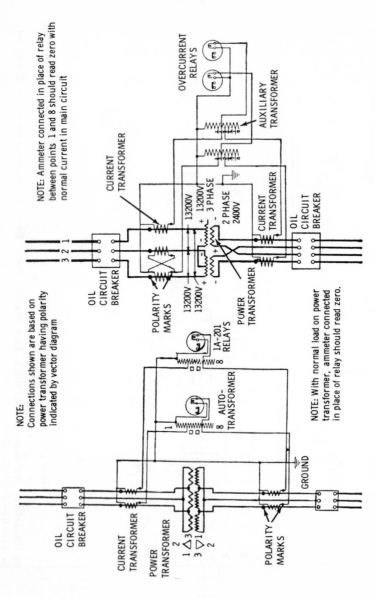

Current-Differential Protection of Transformer Connected Three Phase to Two Phase.

Current-Differential Protection of Transformer Connected Delta-Delta.

INDUSTRIAL
CONTROL WIRING
OF
DC MOTORS

DC MOTOR STARTER WITH MAGNETIC
CONTACTOR AND THREE CONTROL STATIONS

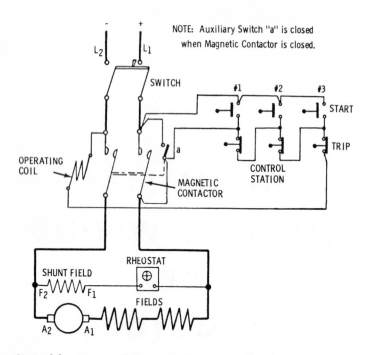

Motor Control by Means of Magnetic Contactor—The above diagram will facilitate the understanding of the advantage connected with the usage of a magnetic contactor, especially when it is desired to operate the motor from any one of several places, as, for example, in operation of a conveyor. The line magnetic contactors have a large following for the following reasons: (a) if the motor is to be operated at frequent intervals, less physical effort will be exerted to operate the push button than that required to close a heavy breaker; (b) A number of control stations may be arranged to operate the motor from several locations, thus saving time and providing for a more economical operation, especially since the control wiring consists of small inexpensive wire.

Operation—When the starting button is operated a circuit is formed through the operating coil, causing the contactor to close its contact. The magnetic contactor does not open after the finger is removed from the starting button, because a new circuit is accomplished through auxiliary switch "A" by means of which the operating coil is energized. To stop the motor the trip button is operated. This action de-energizes the operating coil, causing the contactor to open, and disconnects the motor from its source.

DC MOTOR STARTER WITH MAGNETIC CONTACTOR AND OVERLOAD RELAY

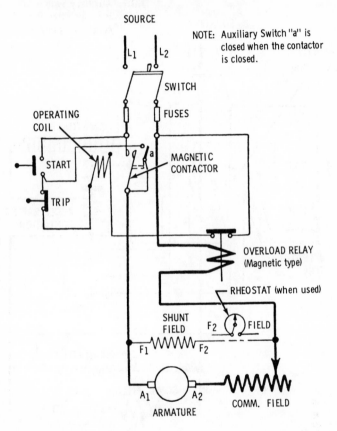

SOURCE

NOTE: Auxiliary Switch "a" is closed when the contactor is closed.

L₁ L₂

SWITCH

OPERATING COIL

FUSES

START

MAGNETIC CONTACTOR

TRIP

OVERLOAD RELAY (Magnetic type)

RHEOSTAT (when used)

SHUNT FIELD

F₂ FIELD

F₁ WWWWW F₂

A₁ A₂

COMM. FIELD

ARMATURE

Operation—When the starting button is operated a circuit is formed through the operating coil, causing the contactor to close its contact. The magnetic contactor does not open after the finger is removed from the starting button, because a new circuit is accomplished through Auxiliary switch "A" by means of which the operating coil is energized.

To stop the motor the trip button is operated. This action de-energizes the operating coil, causing the contactor to open and disconnects the motor from its source. The overload relay is set to operate at a certain overload depending upon the particular operating conditions but should in no case be caused to operate on the motor starting current.

DC COUNTER EMF STARTER WITH TWO CONTACTORS

NOTE: Auxiliary Switch "a"
is closed when the
contactor is closed.

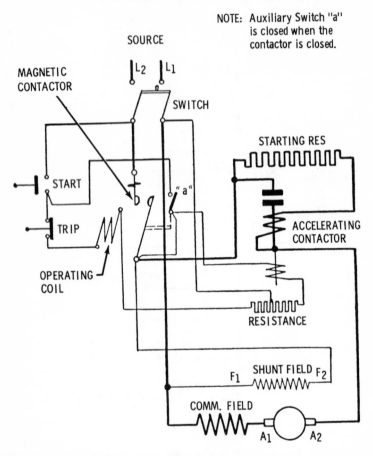

Operation—With reference to the diagram, this starter functions as follows: When the starting button is pressed the operating coil is energized through a resistance, closing the magnetic contactor. After the finger has been removed from the starting button, the lower section of the accelerating contactor is placed in series with the magnetic contactor operating coil. This reduces the power required to hold the magnetic contactor closed and the magnetizing action of the lower accelerating contactor coil aids the upper section of the coil, closing this contactor when the armature voltage has reached a predetermined value. The motor is disconnected from its source by means of operation of the trip button which de-energizes the operating coil, causing the magnetic contactor to open.

DC MOTOR STARTER WITH SERIES
LOCKOUT CONTACTORS

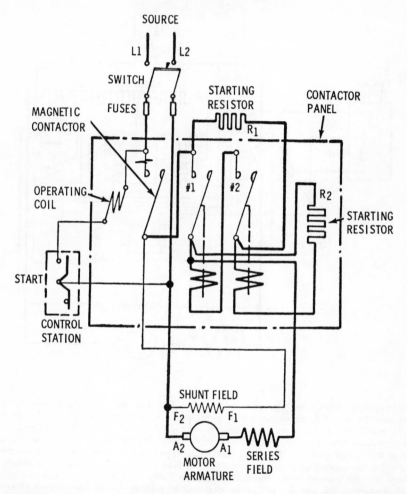

Operation—Closing the starting button causes the magnetic contactor to close, connecting the motor to the line through all the series resistances. Contactor #2 closes its contacts as soon as the current has reached the value at which the contactor is set to operate. This shunts out R_2 and cuts in coil of contactor #1 in the circuit. As the accelerating process of the motor continues the current decreases and contactor #1 closes, connecting the motor directly across the line.

DC MOTOR STARTING BY MEANS OF
SERIES CONTACTORS

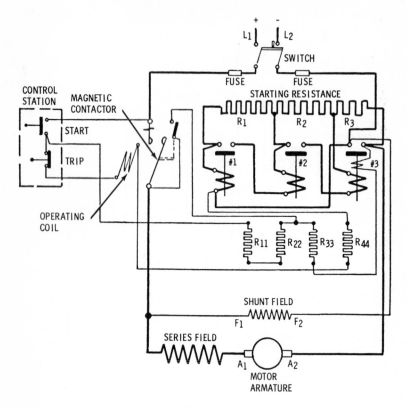

Operation—After the magnetic switch is closed and the starting button is released, R_{11} and R_{22} are connected in series with the closing coil. At the closing of the magnetic contactor, the shunt field is connected directly across the line and current passes from L_1 through the series field, armature, the whole starting resistance and the coil of contactor #1 to L_2. Contactor #1 will close when the current reaches a value corresponding to its setting. With the closing of this contactor, R_1 is shunted out and the current flows through the series field, armature, R_3, R_2 and the coils of contactors #2 and #1 to L_2. The decrease in current due to the closing of contactor will cause contactor #2 to be locked out. Contactor #2 closes as soon as the current has reached a value to which it is set. This action again shunts out R_2 and coil of contactor #3 is brought into the circuit. Contactor #3 closes when its current setting has been reached, shunting out R_3, finally connecting the motor across its supply source. In this starting method, contactors #1 and #2 drop out while contactor #3 is held closed by the holding coil shown at the top of the contactor.

DC MOTOR STARTER EMPLOYING SERIES RELAYS

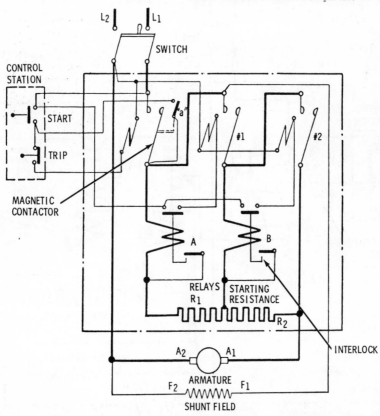

NOTE: AUXILIARY SWITCH "a" IS CLOSED
WHEN MAGNETIC CONTACTOR IS CLOSED.

Operation—In this method of motor starting, an interlock type of relay is provided for each step of starting resistance. The relay contacts are normally held closed by gravity, although the magnetic force produced by the coil holds it open until the current has reached a set value. The starting method is as follows: The magnetic switch is closed in the usual manner, causing the current to flow from L_1 through relay coil A, resistances R_1 and R_2 and the motor armature, to L_2. When the starting current reaches the value for which relay A is set, its contacts close; this in turn causes contactor #1 to close. This action shunts out relay A and R_1 and provides a path for the current through R_2, relay coil B, and contactor #1. This operation is repeated until all the contactors are closed, at which time the relay coils are shunted out and the motor is connected directly across the line.

DC STARTER WITH CURRENT-LIMITING CONTACTORS

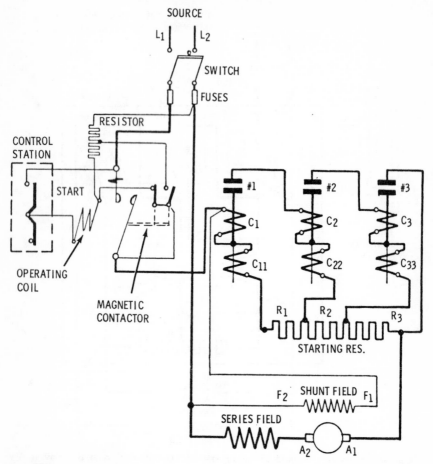

Operation—When the starting button is closed, energizing the operating coil, the magnetic contactor closes. The starting current flows from L_2 through the series field, armature, starting resistance, and contactor coils C_1 and C_{11} to L_1. The shunt field is connected directly across the line. After the current through contractor #1 has reached the contactor setting value, this contactor closes its contact, shunting out coils C_1, C_{11} and R_1. This operation provides a current path through C_{22}, C_2 via contactor #1 and its coil C_1. After the current through contactor #2 has reached the contactor setting value, this contactor closes, and so the process is repeated until all the contactors are closed, at which time the motor is connected directly across the line.

DC COMPOUND-WOUND MOTOR WITH
SERIES RESISTANCE STARTER

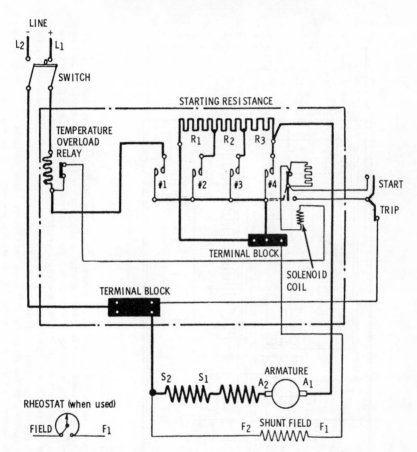

Operation—When the starting button is pressed, contactor #1 closes, connecting the entire starting resistance in series with the motor. After a predetermined interval of time, contactor #2 is engaged, shunting out resistance R_1. In a similar manner each one of the contactors will serve to cut out the resistance preceding it until the entire resistance has been shunted out and the motor is connected across the line at normal voltage. The overload relay serves to protect the motor against overcurrent and may be set to operate to suit individual operating conditions. When the overcurrent exceeds the setting value of the relay the relay contacts open, deenergizing the solenoid coil which trips the contactors, disconnecting the motor from its supply source.

DC COMPOUND-WOUND MOTOR CONTROL
FOR STEEL MILL, MAIN ROLL DRIVE

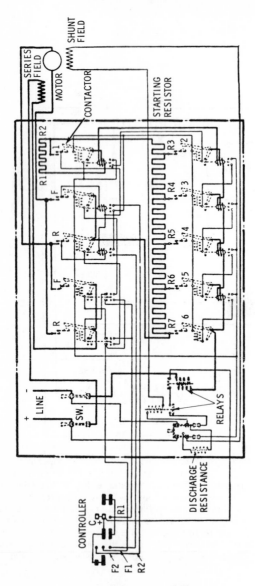

Operation—Direct-current motors for motor-driven reversing mills, are used only on low-voltage circuits usually not exceeding 250 volts, consequently remote control is easily secured and contactors can be used with entire satisfaction for closing, opening and reversing the armature circuit and for cutting out resistance. In addition to the disconnecting switches shown, a combined shunt-field and control switch is supplied which renders it impossible to open the shunt field without at the same time disconnecting the armature from the line. An overload relay and shunt-field relay afford protection respectively in case of overloads or accidental opening of the shunt field. Current-limit relays insure uniform acceleration, while no-voltage protection is secured automatically since the contactors are actuated by line potential.

212

WIRING DIAGRAM AND FRONT VIEW OF TYPICAL FACE-PLATE CONTROLLER

NOTE:
WHEN PERMANENT SLIP RESISTANCE IS FURNISHED, CONNECT AS PER DOTTED LINES AT A, B & C.

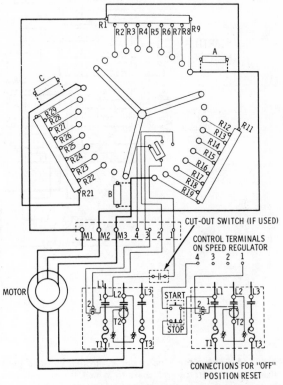

Operation—As shown in the illustrations, the segments are installed in a circle on the face of the controller. Connections from these segments to the collector plates (designated A and A₁) are established by means of two arms which by a movement in either direction change the resistance in the circuit to be operated, as indicated in the wiring diagram. Thus when the handle is moved in a forward direction sections of the starting resistance are cut out in steps, causing the armature to increase its speed.

On the other hand when the arm is moved in a reversed direction, the current becomes reversed in the armature (only) which causes the motor to rotate in the opposite direction. Finally, when the arm is in the off position, the arm rests on two insulating plates, in which case the operating handle is the vertical position.

WIRING DIAGRAM AND INSIDE VIEW OF
TYPICAL DRUM CONTROLLER

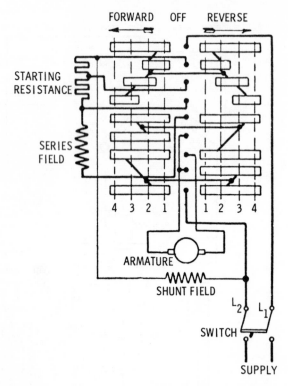

Operation of Controller—The drum controller consists generally of a drum cylinder insulated from its central shaft to which the operating handle is attached. To facilitate the operation, copper segments are attached to the drum. These segments are connected to and/or insulated from one another as shown in the diagram of connections. A series of stationary fingers are arranged to contact with the segments. These fingers are insulated from one another but interconnected to the starting resistance and the motor circuit. The drum assembly has a notched wheel keyed to the central shaft, the function of which is to indicate to the operator when complete contacts are made. With reference to the diagram, when the controller is moved forward one notch, the fingers are in position 1. The current then flows from L_1, through all the series resistance, to L_2, and the motor starts rotating. When the handle is moved further the resistance is gradually cut out of the armature circuit and inserted in the field circuit. Finally, when the handle is turned to notch 4, all the resistance has been transferred from the armature to the field circuit, and the motor is running at full speed.

REVERSING CONTROLLER FOR DC MOTOR

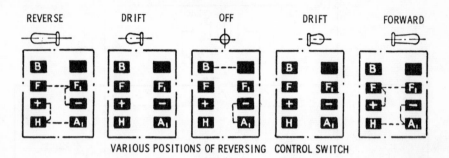

REVERSE   DRIFT   OFF   DRIFT   FORWARD

VARIOUS POSITIONS OF REVERSING CONTROL SWITCH

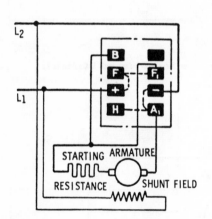

STARTING ARMATURE

RESISTANCE   SHUNT FIELD

FINGER   SEGMENT

Operation—In some industrial processes a combination of dynamic braking and reversing is required. A common type of switch for this requirement is shown, together with a sequence in which the contacts are made. With reference to diagrams, L_1 and L_2 are connected to the positive and negative terminals. When the handle is in the reverse position, H and A_1 are positive, while F and F_1 are negative. If the handle is turned to forward position F, F_1 and H, A_1 exchange polarities. Suppose that the motor armature is connected between A_1 and F_1; the current through it and hence the direction of rotation will be reversed as the handle is turned from reverse to forward. Therefore this switch is fundamentally a reversing switch and may be utilized in connection with any starter.

DYNAMIC BRAKING

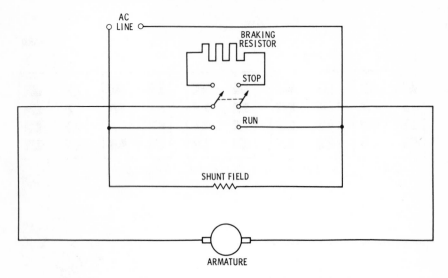

Connections for Dynamic Braking of a Series-Wound DC Motor.

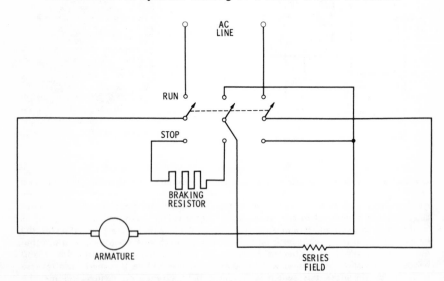

Connections for Dynamic Braking of a Shunt-Wound DC Motor.

WIRING DIAGRAM OF REVERSING AND
DYNAMIC BRAKING CONTROLLER FOR DC MOTOR

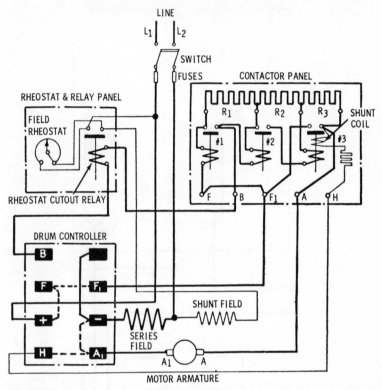

Operation—As indicated in the diagram the shunt field is connected directly across the line through the rheostat when the switch is in a closed position. With reference to the diagram of the drum controller wiring, with the main switch in the forward position the line circuit is from L_1 to F_1, through all the starting resistance, motor armature to the negative terminal and L_2. Contractors #1, #2 and #3 close their contacts in sequence as the armature current decreases, which connects the motor directly across its supply source.

Dynamic Braking—This is effected by turning the handle of the control switch from the forward to the off position. Segments in the control switch connect A_1 and B together, placing sections R_2 and R_3 of the starting resistance across the armature. This circuit provides dynamic braking action, causing the motor to slow down rapidly. As the motor slows down the generation voltage diminishes and the current through the resistance decreases as a consequence, tending to reduce the braking torque.

CONNECTION DIAGRAMS FOR DC
COMPOUND-WOUND MOTORS

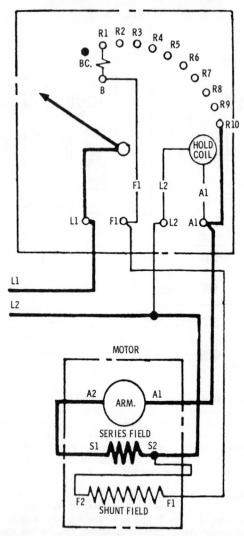

**Typical Wiring Diagram Showing Connection of a Compound-Wound Motor
to Its Face-Plate Starter**—For shunt-wound motors the series field coil is omitted.
This starter is used for starting duty only.

CONNECTION DIAGRAMS FOR DC
COMPOUND-WOUND MOTORS

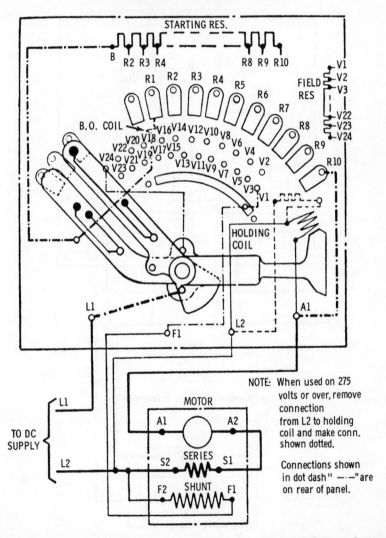

Typical Wiring Diagram Showing Connection of a Compound-Wound Motor to Its Face-Plate Starter—For shunt-wound motors the series field coil is omitted. This starter is used for starting and speed regulating duty by field control only.

CONNECTION DIAGRAMS FOR DC
COMPOUND-WOUND MOTORS

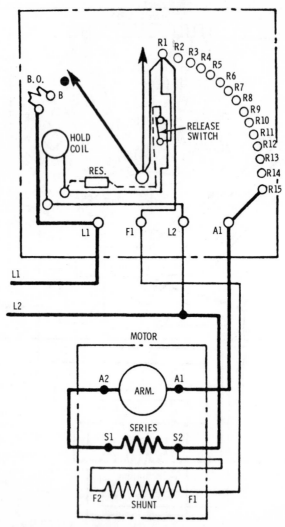

Typical Wiring Diagram Showing Connection of a Compound-Wound Motor to Its Face-Plate Starter—For shunt-wound motors the series field coil is omitted. This starter is for speed regulating duty—50% speed reduction by armature control.

CONNECTION DIAGRAMS FOR DC COMPOUND-WOUND MOTORS

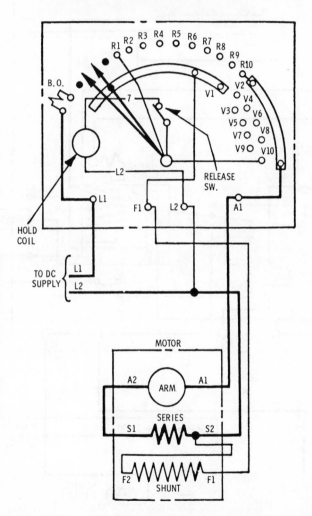

Typical Wiring Diagram, Showing Connection of a Compound-Wound Motor to Its Face-Plate Starter—For shunt-wound motors the series field coil is omitted. This starter is used for speed regulating duty—50% speed reduction by armature control and 25% increase by field control.

DC REDUCED-VOLTAGE STARTER

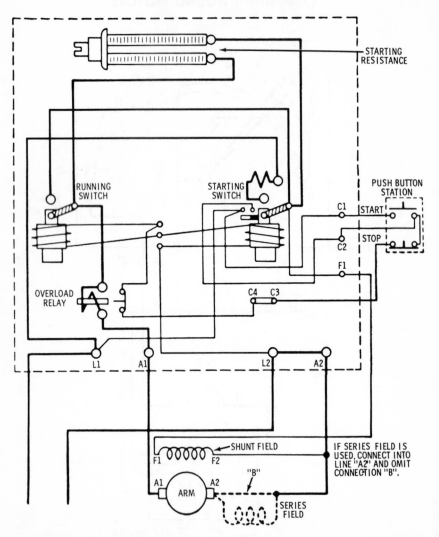

Connections for Reduced-Voltage Starting of Shunt, Series or Compound-Wound Direct-Current Motors—The length of time the starting resistors are in the circuit is determined by a time-limit starting switch such as the fluid dashpot type.

INDUSTRIAL
CONTROL WIRING
OF
AC MOTORS

MOTOR-CONTROL METHODS

The Functions of Motor Control—The elementary functions of any motor control are starting, stopping and reversing the motor. These functions however, are only a few of the many contributions which the control renders to efficient operation of modern electric drives. Among the common functions of motor control required in motor installations are:

1. Motor Starting—This includes the basic function of starting and stopping the motor, including protection from overload and under voltage when required.

2. Motor Starting and Reversing—This includes the basic function of starting the motor where the direction of rotation of the motor is changed at will of the operator.

3. Motor Starting and Speed Regulation—Basic function of starting and stopping the motor involving speed regulation or adjustment of motor speed as by rheostat control.

4. Motor Starting, Reversing and Speed Regulation—Basic function of starting, stopping or reversing the motor involving speed regulation as by rheostat control.

5. Motor Starting and Speed Selection—Basic functions of starting and stopping the motor, involving selection of one of several basic speeds as by pole changing.

6. Motor Starting, Reversing and Speed Selection—Basic functions of starting, stopping and reversing, including selection of one of several basic speeds.

With respect to the general construction and method of starting and control required in motor installations as:

7. Across the Line Starter—This consists of a line switch (with protection as may be required) for connecting the motor directly across the supply line. This method of starting is also referred to as "full-voltage starting."

8. Starting Rheostat—Also referred to as the face-panel type. This is a type of rheostat whose stationary contacts are mounted upon the face of an insulating panel whose surface is a plane, the contacts being arranged in the form of an arc (or arcs) of a circle and the moveable contact (or contacts) being mounted upon a pivoted switch arm (or arms).

9. Primary Resistor Starter—A starter which provides reduced voltage to the primary of the motor by inserting resistance in the primary circuit during acceleration. The device includes the necessary switching mechanism, which may be manually or magnetically operated.

10. Secondary Resistor Starter—A starter which reduces the primary starting current by inserting resistance in the secondary circuit, usually the rotor

MOTOR-CONTROL METHODS

of a wound-rotor motor during acceleration. The device includes the necessary switching mechanism, which may be manually or magnetically operated.

11. Compensator or Autotransformer Starter—A starter which provides for reduced voltage starting by means of a compensator or autotransformer from which a predetermined fractional part of the winding is tapped off to produce voltage reduction to suit the particular starting load. The device includes the necessary switching mechanism to switch from the tap to full voltage and also to open the circuit of the compensator winding.

12. Star-Delta Starter—A star-delta starter is one which is applicable for starting of motors which have their windings arranged for full rated operation, with windings connected in delta, and arranged for starting at reduced voltage with windings connected in star.

13. Magnetic Controller—One wherein the main circuits are made and broken by magnetically operated switches controlled by a master switch located either within the controller or at any desired distance from the main controller.

With respect to the operation of the control circuit, magnetic controllers may be subdivided as follows:

14. Nonautomatic—Where the operator is responsible for all control functions of starting, stopping and accelerating the motor.

15. Semiautomatic—Where the rate of acceleration after starting by the operator, is dependent upon accelerating contactors, which are adjusted to function under predetermined conditions of currents, voltages and time.

16. Full Automatic—Where all basic functions including starting or stopping of the motor, are performed without the necessity of manual direction in any degree after being initially energized.

With respect to their type for operating magnetic controllers, the sub-classification of master switches may be made as follows:

17. Drum Switch—In general for nonautomatic types of controllers.

18. Push Button—In general for semiautomatic types of controllers.

19. Automatic Switch—Operated by float, pressure, etc., for full automatic controllers.

20. Emergency-Run Feature—Provides a means of temporarily rendering the overload device inoperative during an emergency.

With respect to the proximity of the master switch, magnetic controllers may be subclassified as follows:

21. Distant Motor Control—Where the master switch is mounted apart from the main control panel.

MOTOR-CONTROL METHODS

22. Local Motor Control—Where the master switch may be combined with the main control panel.

The service classification of control resistors with reference to the duty period are:

23. Continuous Rating—Where the load is required to be carried for an unlimited period.

24. Periodic Rating—Where the load can be carried for alternate periods of load and rest.

25. Standard Periodic Rating—Where the starting and intermittent duty may be standardized as light, heavy, or extra heavy starting, or intermittent duty classifications.

The kind of protection to be provided required may be termed as:

26. Low- or Under-Voltage Protection—Operates to cause and maintain the interruption of the main power or reduction or failure of voltage.

27. Low- or Under-Voltage Release—Operates to cause the interruption of power upon reduction or failure of voltage, but not to maintain the interruption of power upon return of voltage.

28. Overload Protection—Operates to protect against excessive current to cause and maintain the interruption of current not in excess of six times the rated motor current.

29. Short-Circuit Protection—Where the overload protection does not provide for short-circuit protection, such short-circuit protection shall be provided as by fuses.

30. Single-Phase Protection or Indication—Where required, shall indicate and protect the personnel and equipment upon the failure of any part of the circuit which would cause an open phase.

MOTOR-PROTECTIVE DEVICES

The functions of motor protective devices are to protect the motor against certain abnormal conditions, such as:

1. Overloads.

2. Short circuits.

3. Under voltage, etc.

This includes devices which function on the basis of temperature, voltage, frequency, or time, and cause the switching mechanism to operate when a predetermined set of conditions exist.

MOTOR-CONTROL METHODS

Overload Relays—These devices are of two general types, namely:
1. Thermal overload relay, and
2. Dash-pot overload relay.

Thermal and dash-pot overload relays are again divided into two types as:
1. Hand reset, and
2. Automatic reset.

As the name denotes, hand reset relays must be reset by hand after having tripped (usually by pressing a button projecting through the enclosing case) whereas the automatic reset types reset themselves automatically.

Thermal Overload Relay—The thermal overload relay consists of a heater coil which is connected directly to the line of the motor, and which heats up directly in the proportion of current flowing through it. The thermostatic metal is made up of two metals rolled together and wound into a spiral. The two metals have different expansion coefficients so the spiral will unwind as it heats up. A shaft through the center of the spiral and anchored to the end of it will rotate and actuate the switching mechanism.

A Two-Pole Temperature Overload Relay—NOTE: Cover removed from unit to show thermostatic metal strip.

Because one end is solidly anchored, all of the movement occurs at the free end.

MOTOR-CONTROL METHODS

A relay of this type is quite accurate and its operating characteristics are well defined. It is possible to design a heater that will raise the temperature of the thermostatic strip at the same rate as the temperature in the motor with which it is being used, and so adjust the relay that it will trip the control contacts when the temperature of the motor has reached the allowable maximum.

Because some time is required to transmit the heat from the heater coil to the thermostatic strip, it is not affected by momentary current increases. This makes it possible to start the motor with an inrush of six to ten times normal current without tripping the relay.

Dashpot Overload Relay—The dashpot overload relay uses the mechanical retardation principle of a dashpot to retard the movement of a core in a magnetic field, produced by a solenoid coil in series with the motor leads. Such an arrangement is affected by the quality of the mechanical clearance between piston and cylinder wall, changes in viscosity of the dashpot oil caused by temperature variations and other extraneous conditions tending to upset its accuracy.

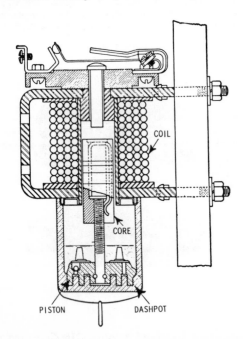

Typical Dashpot, Magnetic-Type Overload Relay, with Oil Dashpots to Give Inverse Time Tripping Characteristics.

MOTOR-CONTROL METHODS

Under-Voltage Protection—Under-voltage or low-voltage protection as it is sometimes called is defined as: The effect of a device operative on the reduction or failure of voltage, to cause and maintain the interruption of power to the main circuit.

With reference to the diagram on the next page, under-voltage protection is provided for in the following manner: Contactor **M** handles the motor circuit. It contains a normally-open contactor holding interlock **B,** which closes when the contactor is closed.

The two-button, push-button station consists of a normally open **start** contact **C** and a normally closed **stop** contact **D.** When contact is made momentarily at **C,** by pressing the start button, the contactor coil **M** is energized and contactor **M** closes, which in turn closes the interlock circuit **B.** It will be noted that the interlock **B** parallels the start contact **C.** The contactor is, therefore, held in through the interlock circuit **B,** even after the start contact C opens up when the finger is removed from the button.

In the case of voltage failure, coil **M** is de-energized and contactor **M** opens, which in turn opens interlock circuit **B.** When voltage returns, the contactor will not close until the circuit is again established at **C** by pushing the start button.

Under-Voltage Release—Under-voltage or low-voltage release is defined as: The effect of a device operative on reduction or failure of voltage to cause the interruption of power to the main circuit, but not to prevent re-establishment of the main circuit on return of voltage.

With reference to the diagram page 231, under-voltage release is provided for in the following manner: The control consists of a contactor **M** for handling the motor circuit, and a maintained contact switch **B.** Switch **B** can be a knife switch, a float switch, a pressure switch or a maintained contact push-button station whose contacts close and remain closed regardless of the voltage on them.

To start the motor, the control switch **B** is closed. This energizes the contactor coil **M**; the contactor **M** closes and the motor is connected to the line. Now if voltage fails, the coil **M** is de-energized and contactor **M** opens. Nothing happens to contact **B** as a result of the failure.

When this type of control is used on certain machines, such as saws, millers, etc. there is always danger if an operator returns to his machine and attempts to remove the saw or milling head, not realizing that the machine has stopped because of the momentary voltage failure. By providing under-voltage protection this hazard is eliminated, because the motor cannot restart when the power returns after a voltage failure, until the operator presses the start button.

MOTOR-CONTROL METHODS

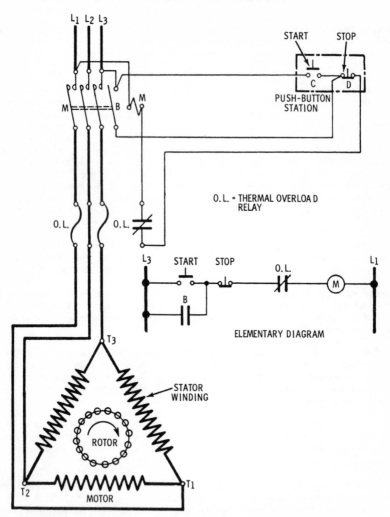

L₁ L₂ L₃

START   STOP

M   B   M

PUSH-BUTTON
STATION

O. L. = THERMAL OVERLOAD
RELAY

O.L.   O.L.

L₃   START   STOP   O.L.   L₁

B   M

ELEMENTARY DIAGRAM

T₃

STATOR
WINDING

ROTOR

T₂   T₁

MOTOR

Fundamental Wiring Diagram of Under-Voltage Protection as Employed on a Manually Operated Squirrel-Cage Induction Motor—It should be noted that any combination of control sequence for under-voltage protection can be obtained by applying these two fundamental rules: (1) Wire all stop buttons in series with the holding coil, with each other, and with the electrical interlock. (2) Wire all start buttons in parallel with each other and with the interlock.

MOTOR-CONTROL METHODS

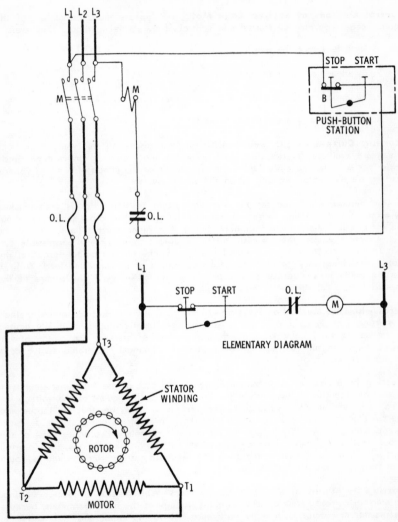

Fundamental Wiring Diagram Showing Method of Wiring to Obtain Under-Voltage Release—Under-voltage release allows the control to drop out if for any reason the power source voltage is inadequate, but when the voltage again reaches sufficient value the control will function automatically to connect the apparatus to the line through the proper starting sequence.

MOTOR-CONTROL METHODS

Control Methods of Squirrel-Cage Motors—Polyphase induction motors of the squirrel-cage type may be started and controlled by several methods. They are:

1. Directly across the line.

2. By means of autotransformers.

3. By means of resistors or reactors in series with the stator winding.

4. By means of the star-delta method.

Starting Current-Torque Relationship—Before discussing the various methods which are available for reducing starting current and improving line-voltage conditions, it is important to have a thorough knowledge of the effects of reduced voltage starting on the motor, as well as on the power system.

Any method which reduces the starting current to the motor is accomplished by a reduction in starting torque. Therefore, it is essential to know something about the load-torque characteristics in determining if a given current limitation can be met. In other words, there are boundary conditions in which the permissible current to be taken from the line would not provide the needed output torque at the motor shaft, necessary for the successful acceleration of its connected load. With all starting methods, the torque of a squirrel-cage motor varies as the square of the applied voltage at the motor terminals.

Across-the-Line Method of Starting—This is generally the most economical method of starting, but on account of the large starting current required, is usually limited to motors up to 5 horsepower. With this method of starting, the motor is connected direct to full line voltage by means of a manually operated switch or a magnetic contactor.

Starting by Means of Autotransformer—In the case of the autotransformer type of starting, the current taken from the line varies as the square of the voltage applied to the motor terminals, and it is convenient to remember that the torque and line currents are reduced at the same rate. Thus, an autotransformer starter designed to apply 80% of the line voltage to the motor terminals will produce 64% of the torque that would have been developed if the motor had been started on full voltage, and will at the same time draw 64% as much current from the line as would have been required for full-voltage starting.

Starting by Means of Resistors or Reactors—With resistor or reactor starting, the starting current varies directly with the voltage at the motor terminals, because the resistor or reactor is in series with each line to the motor and must carry the same current that flows in each motor terminal.

It is evident therefore, that the resistor and reactor type of reduced voltage starting requires more line current in amperes per unit of torque in foot-pounds than does the autotransformer type.

MOTOR-CONTROL METHODS

Thus, if a motor connected to a loaded centrifugal pump is started with 80% tap on the autotransformer, the initial torque is 64%. If, on the other hand, the motor were started with a primary resistor, limiting the starting voltage to 65% of line voltage, the initial torque would only be 42.25%.

On some power systems, it is necessary to meet a restriction on the rate of current increase in starting. The rate of increase of current is determined to meet the conditions as they exist at that particular point on the system where the motor is started.

Starting By Means of the Star-Delta Method—Three-phase induction motors of the squirrel-cage type may occasionally be started by the star-delta method. This starting method is associated only with motors designed for their full power with the delta-connected, three-phase winding. There must also be provided additional leads from the motor which when regrouped will result in a star arrangement of the three-phase winding.

There will be six main leads required from the motor to accomplish the switch from start across the line (star-connection) to run across the line (delta-connection). The starting connection is always star, since the voltage is $1/\sqrt{3}$ or 57.8% of the delta or line voltage.

From the foregoing it follows that this type of reduced-voltage starter (which is limited to 57.8% of line voltage at starting) can be employed only where the motor has a light starting load. In all other applications higher starting voltages are obtained with the resistor, reactors or autotransformers as previously outlined.

MOTOR-CONTROL METHODS

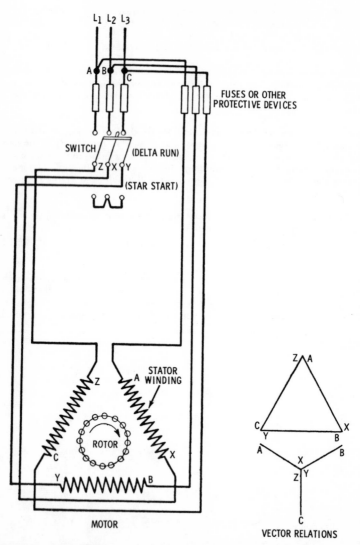

Typical Connection Diagram when Star-Delta Method of Starting Is Used for Squirrel-Cage Induction Motor—In the case of large motors, that is, motors rated above 5 h.p., a special oil switch controller is most commonly employed.

MOTOR-CONTROL METHODS

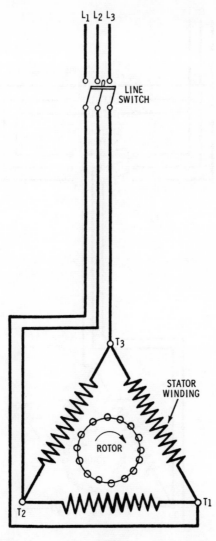

Fundamental Wiring Diagram of Typical Across-the-Line Nonreversible, Single-Speed, Manually Operated, Squirrel-Cage Induction Motor.

MOTOR-CONTROL METHODS

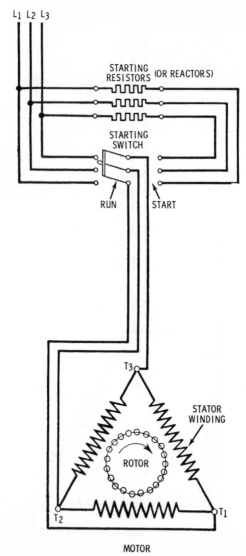

Fundamental Wiring Diagram of Typical Reduced Voltage, Nonreversible, Single-Speed, Manually Operated, Squirrel-Cage Induction Motor.

MOTOR-CONTROL METHODS

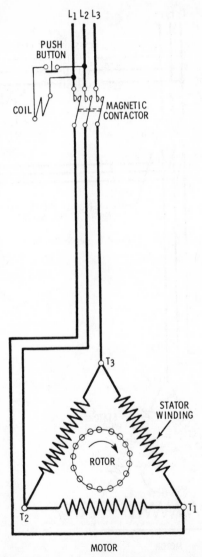

Fundamental Wiring Diagram of Typical Across-the-Line, Nonreversible, Single-Speed, Magnetically Operated, Squirrel-Cage Induction Motor.

237

MOTOR-CONTROL METHODS

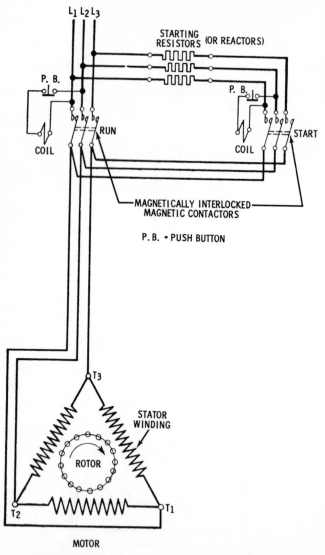

L₁ L₂ L₃

STARTING RESISTORS (OR REACTORS)

P. B.

COIL

RUN

P. B.

COIL

START

MAGNETICALLY INTERLOCKED
MAGNETIC CONTACTORS

P. B. - PUSH BUTTON

T3

STATOR
WINDING

ROTOR

T2   T1

MOTOR

**Fundamental Wiring Diagram of Typical Reduced Voltage, Nonreversible,
Single-Speed, Magnetically Operated, Squirrel-Cage Induction Motor.**

MOTOR-CONTROL METHODS

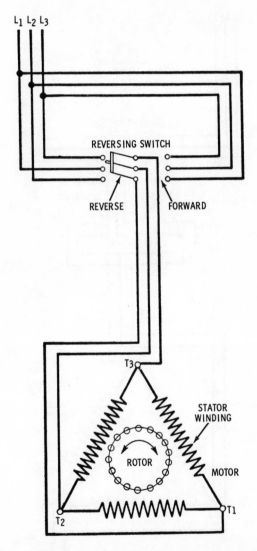

Fundamental Wiring Diagram of Typical Across-the-Line, Reversible, Single-Speed, Manually Operated, Squirrel-Cage Induction Motor.

239

MOTOR-CONTROL METHODS

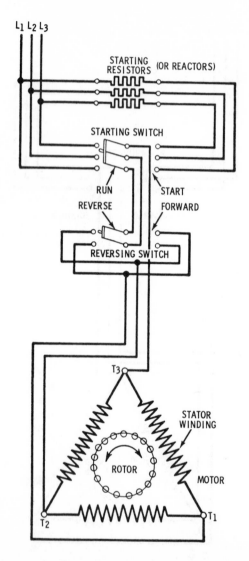

Fundamental Wiring Diagram of Typical Reduced Voltage, Reversible, Single-Speed, Manually Operated, Squirrel-Cage Induction Motor.

MOTOR-CONTROL METHODS

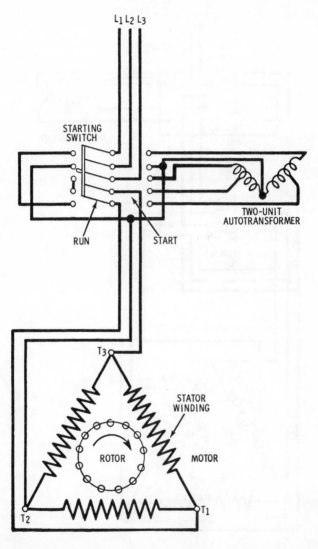

L₁ L₂ L₃

STARTING
SWITCH

TWO-UNIT
AUTOTRANSFORMER

RUN   START

T₃

STATOR
WINDING

ROTOR   MOTOR

T₂   T₁

Fundamental Wiring Diagram of Typical Reduced Voltage, Nonreversible, Single-Speed, Manually Operated, Squirrel-Cage Induction Motor.

241

MOTOR-CONTROL METHODS

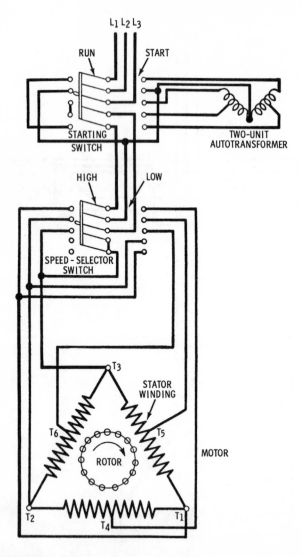

Fundamental Wiring Diagram of Typical Reduced Voltage, Two-Speed Non-reversible, Manually Operated, Squirrel-Cage Induction Motor.

MOTOR-CONTROL METHODS

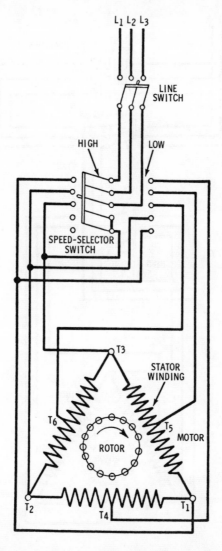

Fundamental Wiring Diagram of Typical Across-the-Line, Two-Speed, Non-reversible, Manually Operated, Squirrel-Cage Induction Motor.

243

MOTOR-CONTROL METHODS

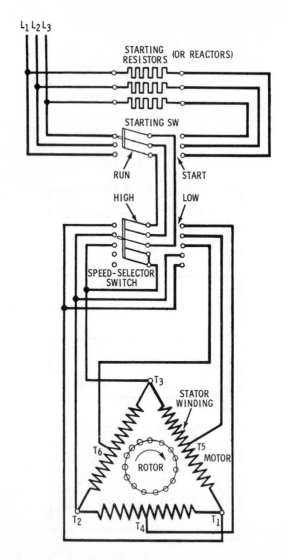

Fundamental Wiring Diagram of Typical Reduced Voltage, Two-Speed, Non-reversible, Manually Operated, Squirrel-Cage Induction Motor.

MOTOR-CONTROL METHODS

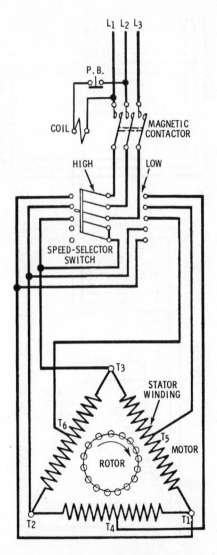

Fundamental Wiring Diagram of Typical Across-the-Line, Two-Speed, Non-reversible, Magnetically Operated, Squirrel-Cage Induction Motor.

245

MOTOR-CONTROL METHODS

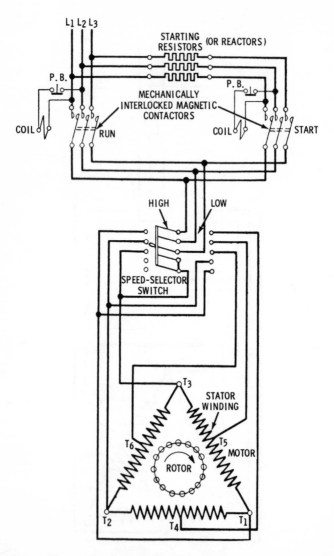

Fundamental Wiring Diagram of Typical Reduced Voltage, Two-Speed, Non-reversible, Magnetically Operated, Squirrel-Cage Induction Motor.

MOTOR-CONTROL METHODS

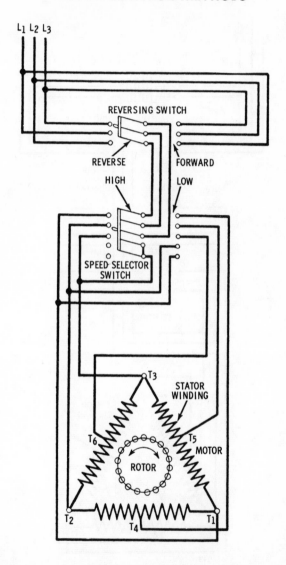

Fundamental Wiring Diagram of Typical Across-the-Line, Two-Speed, Reversible, Manually Operated, Squirrel-Cage Induction Motor.

MOTOR-CONTROL METHODS

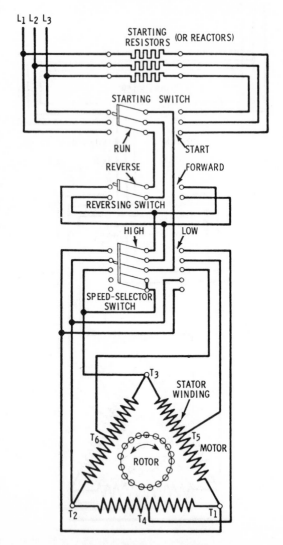

Fundamental Wiring Diagram of Typical Reduced Voltage, Two-Speed Reversible, Manually Operated, Squirrel-Cage Induction Motor.

MOTOR-CONTROL METHODS

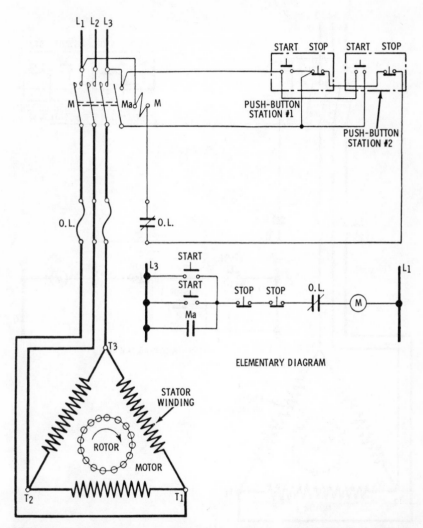

L₁ L₂ L₃

M   Ma   M

START   STOP   START   STOP

PUSH-BUTTON
STATION #1

PUSH-BUTTON
STATION #2

O.L.   O.L.

L₃   START   L₁

START

STOP   STOP   O.L.

Ma   M

ELEMENTARY DIAGRAM

O.L.

T3

STATOR
WINDING

ROTOR

MOTOR

T2   T1

Wiring Diagram of Typical Remotely Controlled, Magnetically Operated, Squirrel-Cage Induction Motor—The push-button circuit consists of two control stations, each with two momentary contacts, one closed and one open. The circuit provides under-voltage protection. The operating duty is: **Start-stop, start-stop.**

MOTOR-CONTROL METHODS

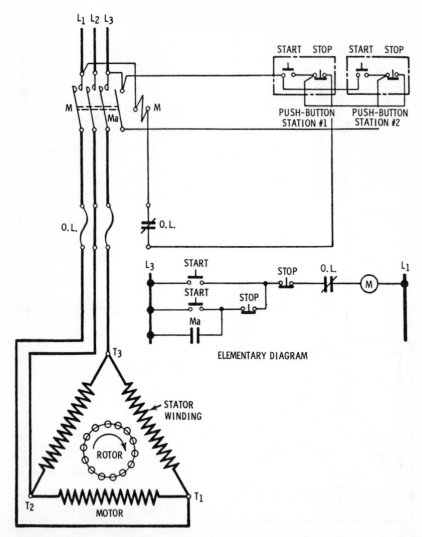

Wiring Diagram of Typical Remotely Controlled, Magnetically Operated, Squirrel-Cage Induction Motor—The push-button circuit consists of two control stations with only three wires between the stations. The circuit provides under-voltage protection. The operating duty is: **Start-stop, start-stop.**

250

MOTOR-CONTROL METHODS

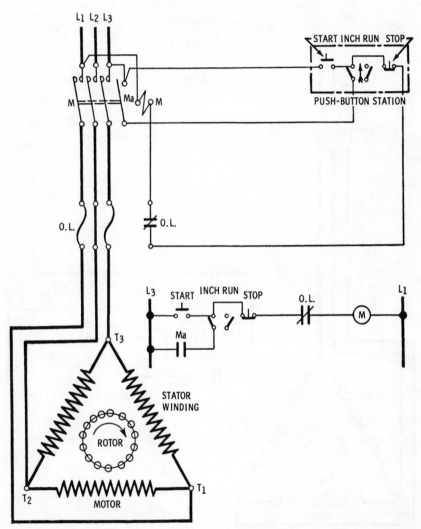

Wiring Diagram of Typical Remotely Controlled, Magnetically Operated, Squirrel-Cage Induction Motor—The push-button circuit consists of one control station, with two momentary-contact buttons and one selector switch. The circuit provides under-voltage protection plus inching. The operation duty is: **Start-run, inch-stop.**

MOTOR-CONTROL METHODS

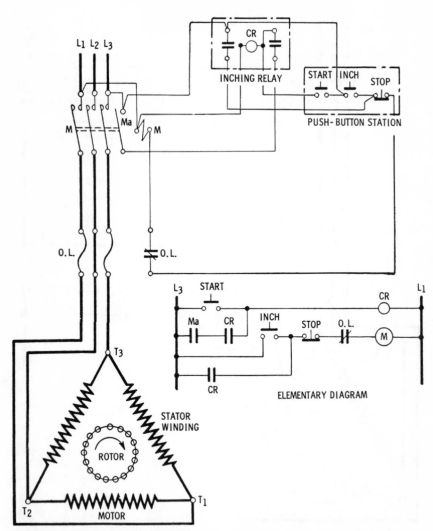

Wiring Diagram of Typical Remotely Controlled, Magnetically Operated, Squirrel-Cage Induction Motor—The push-button circuit consists of one push-button station, with three momentary contacts and an inching relay. The circuit provides under-voltage protection plus foolproof inching. The operating duty is: **Start-inch-stop.**

252

MOTOR-CONTROL METHODS

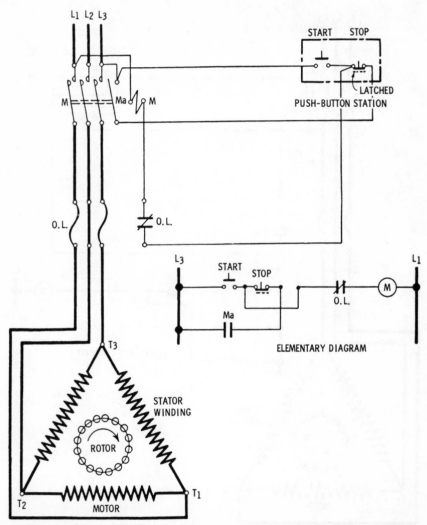

Wiring Diagram of Typical Remotely Controlled, Magnetically Operated, Squirrel-Cage Induction Motor—The push-button circuit consists of one control station with two momentary-control buttons, one open and one closed with safety latch. The circuit provides under-voltage protection. The operating duty is: **Start-stop (on inch for latch).**

MOTOR-CONTROL METHODS

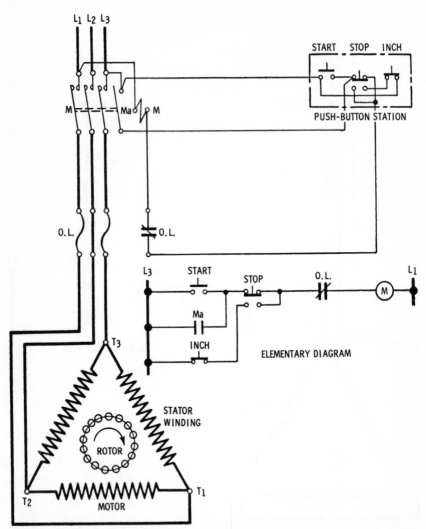

Wiring Diagram of Typical Remotely Controlled, Magnetically Operated, Squirrel-Cage Induction Motor—The push-button circuit consists of one control station, with three momentary-contact buttons of which two are open and one closed. The circuit provides under-voltage protection plus inching by holding down stop button. The operating duty is: **Start-inch-stop.**

MOTOR-CONTROL METHODS

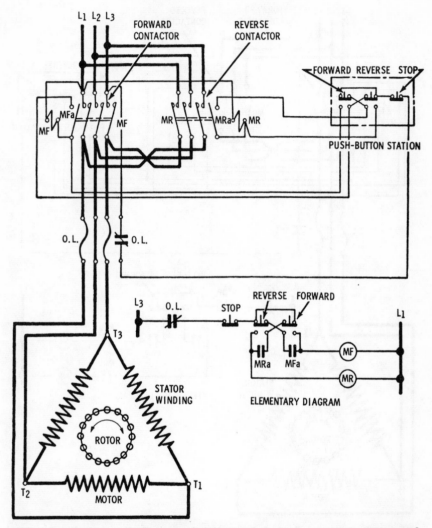

Wiring Diagram of Typical Remotely Controlled Magnetically Operated, Reversible, Squirrel-Cage Induction Motor—The push-button circuit consists of one control station, with three momentary contact buttons, two open and one closed. The circuit provides under-voltage protection, interlocked through push-buttons. The operating duty is: **Forward-reverse-stop.**

MOTOR-CONTROL METHODS

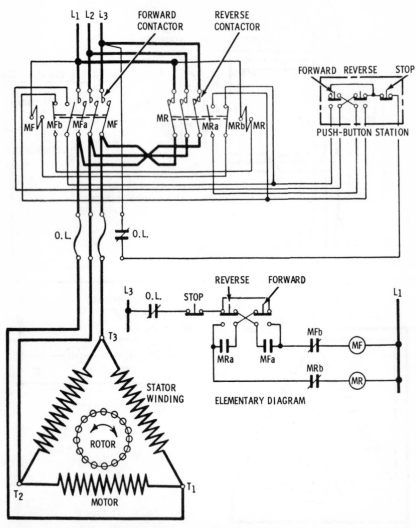

Wiring Diagram of Typical Remotely Controlled, Magnetically Operated, Reversible, Squirrel-Cage Induction Motor—The push-button circuit consists of one control station, with three momentary contact buttons, two open and one closed. The circuit provides under-voltage protection with electrical interlocks. The operating duty is: **Forward-reverse-stop.**

MOTOR-CONTROL METHODS

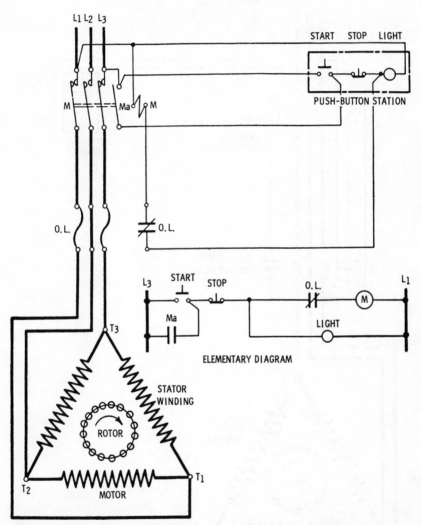

ELEMENTARY DIAGRAM

Wiring Diagram of Typical Remotely Controlled, Magnetically Operated, Squirrel-Cage Induction Motor—The push-button circuit consists of one control station with two momentary control buttons, one open and one closed, plus an indicating light showing operating position of contactor. The circuit provides undervoltage protection. The operating duty is: **Start-stop.**

MOTOR-CONTROL METHODS

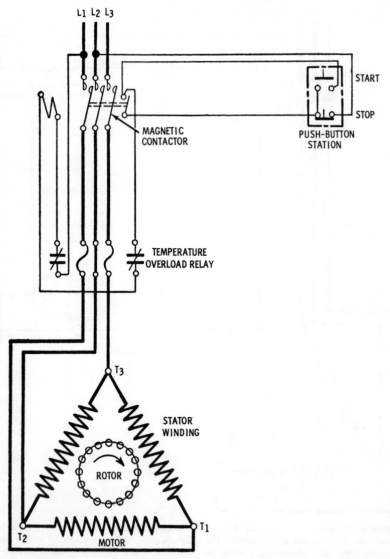

Wiring Diagram of Typical Across-the-Line, Single-Speed, Nonreversible, Magnetically Operated, Squirrel-Cage Induction Motor.

258

MOTOR-CONTROL METHODS

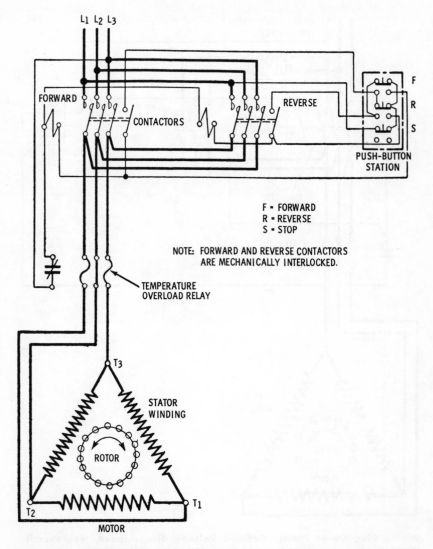

L₁ L₂ L₃

FORWARD

CONTACTORS

REVERSE

PUSH-BUTTON
STATION

F
R
S

F = FORWARD
R = REVERSE
S = STOP

NOTE: FORWARD AND REVERSE CONTACTORS
ARE MECHANICALLY INTERLOCKED.

TEMPERATURE
OVERLOAD RELAY

T₃

STATOR
WINDING

ROTOR

T₂   T₁

MOTOR

**Connection Diagram of Typical Across-the-Line, Single-Speed, Reversible,
Magnetically Operated, Squirrel-Cage, Induction Motor.**

MOTOR-CONTROL METHODS

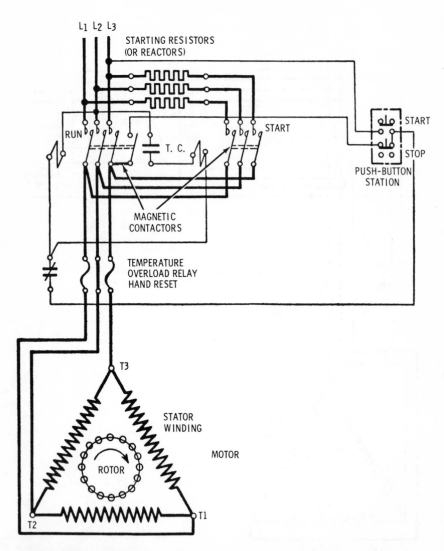

L₁ L₂ L₃

STARTING RESISTORS
(OR REACTORS)

RUN

START

T. C.

START

STOP

PUSH-BUTTON
STATION

MAGNETIC
CONTACTORS

TEMPERATURE
OVERLOAD RELAY
HAND RESET

T3

STATOR
WINDING

MOTOR

ROTOR

T2

T1

Wiring Diagram of Typical Reduced Voltage, Single-Speed, Nonreversible, Magnetically Operated, Squirrel-Cage Induction Motor. In the diagram T.C. is a time closing contact.

ACROSS-THE-LINE AC MOTOR-STARTING ARRANGEMENT

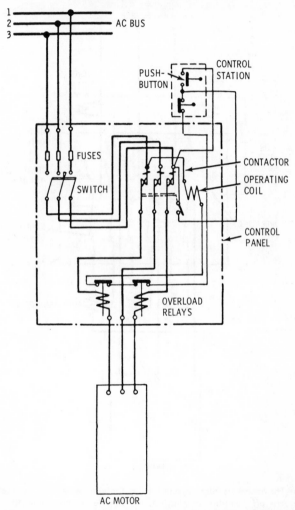

AC BUS

PUSH-BUTTON

CONTROL STATION

FUSES

SWITCH

CONTACTOR

OPERATING COIL

CONTROL PANEL

OVERLOAD RELAYS

AC MOTOR

Operation—This starter consists of a three-pole knife switch and a three-pole magnetically operated contactor and two overload relays with a reset button.

In this system of control, the contacts will open on voltage failure and will remain open after the voltage has been re-established until the start button is operated.

MANUAL COMPENSATOR WITH MAGNETIC
OVERLOAD RELAYS

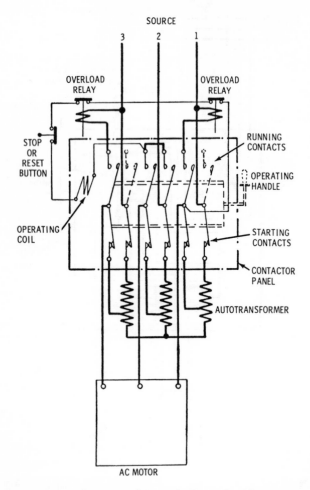

Operation—The motor is disconnected from the line when the contactor operating handle is in the off position. In starting, the handle is thrown to the start position which closes the starting contacts forming connections through the Y-connected autotransformer and reducing the impressed voltage on the motor during the starting period. After normal speed is reached, the operating handle is thrown to the run position, which opens the starting contacts and closes the running contacts, connecting the motor directly across the line.

MANUAL COMPENSATOR WITH THERMAL OVERLOAD RELAY

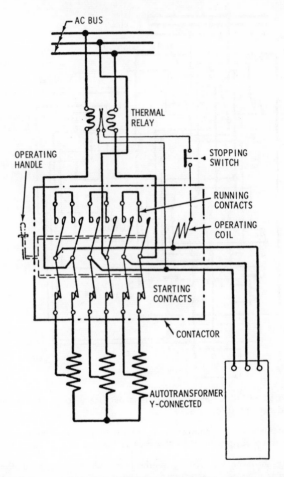

Operation—The starting of the motor is accomplished as follows: With the motor disconnected from the line, the operating handle is in off position.

First Step—Throw the operating handle to the start position. The motor is now connected to the line at reduced voltage through the taps of the autotransformer. **Second Step**—After the motor has reached normal speed, operate the handle to run position; at this time the starting contacts are automatically disengaged, and the motor is connected across the line at full voltage.

STARTING AND REVERSING CONTROL ARRANGEMENT
FOR A THREE-PHASE INDUCTION MOTOR

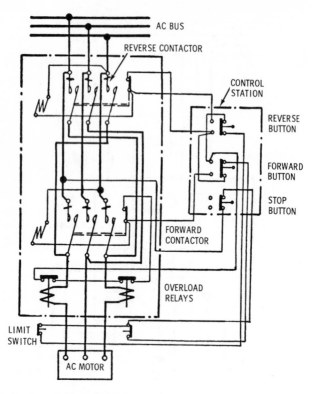

Operation—In some industrial processes it is necessary to run the motor alternately in forward and reverse directions.

This is accomplished by a control arrangement which interchanges the connection of two of the three supply lines to the motor.

In following through the wiring method it will be observed that when the forward button is operated the forward contactor coil will be energized, closing the contactor and connecting the motor to the line. If it is desired to reverse the motor, it is necessary merely to press the reverse button, which opens the circuit of the forward contactor coil and closes the reverse contactor, at the same time interchanging two of the line wires. The motor is now running in the reverse direction. This operating method is not common where large motors are employed due to the fact that a heavy starting current will cause undesirable voltage fluctuation in the power-line system.

RESISTANCE STARTING FOR AC MOTOR

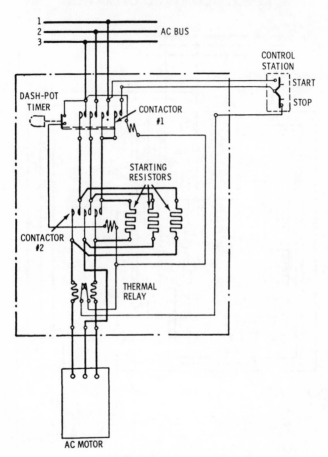

AC MOTOR

Operation—This type of starter operates in the following manner:

The starting current is limited by means of equal resistances in each line wire leading to the motor. These resistances are automatically shunted out after the motor has gained full speed. When the starting button is pressed, contactor #1 is energized causing this contactor to close which connects the motor to the line through the starting resistors. The circuit of the #1 contactor coil is maintained through the time interlock on the dash-pot timer, whose contacts close after a definite time has elapsed. This in turn completes the circuit through the coil of contactor #2, which closes its contacts, shunting out the starting resistance and connecting the motor at full voltage directly across the line.

265

AUTOMATIC STARTING CONTACTOR FOR
REMOTE-CONTROL OPERATION

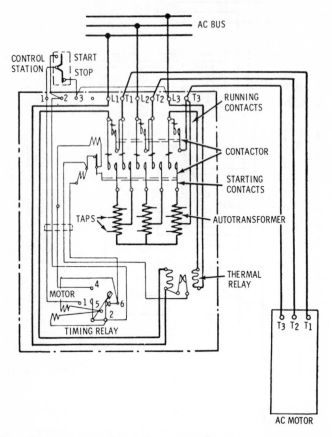

Operation—This type of contactor operates as follows: when the starting button is operated the starting contactor coils become energized, closing the starting contacts of the contactor, thus connecting the motor to the line through a suitable tap of the autotransformer. A circuit which operates the timing relay is also completed, closing the contacts which connect terminals 1 and 2 and thus completing the holding circuit for the relay coil.

Finally after a definite time, depending upon the relay setting, the escapement releases and allows the contact arm to break the contact at 6 and make contact at 4, causing the starting contact to open and the running contacts to close, connecting the motor directly across the line.

DIAGRAM OF INDUCTION-MOTOR CONTROL
FOR STEEL MILL, MAIN ROLL DRIVE

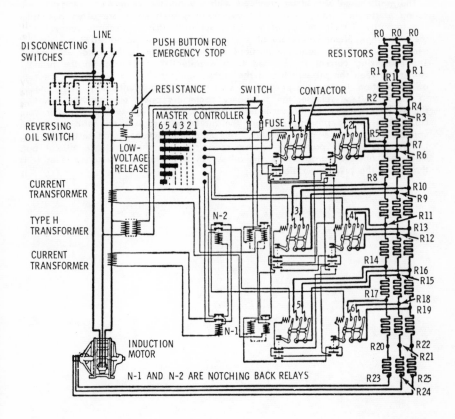

Operation—The essential parts of the control for a large induction motor are relatively few and simple, though sometimes the interlocking devices become exceedingly complex when carried to an unnecessary extent. This diagram shows a typical arrangement of control for such a motor where only occasional partial-speed operation or reversal is required. The incoming line passes through disconnecting switches, by means of which the motor and control can be completely isolated from the line during adjustments or repairs. For high-voltage motors a double-throw, hand-operated reversing oil switch with inverse time-limit overload and no-voltage release is employed. A push button located conveniently in the mill short circuits the no-voltage release, thus tripping out the oil switch and stopping the motor in emergency.   (Text continued)

INDUCTION-MOTOR CONTROL FOR STEEL MILL, MAIN ROLL DRIVE

The motor panel should be provided with a voltmeter, an ammeter, and an indicating wattmeter. Integrating and curve-drawing wattmeters are often desirable. The secondary circuit consists of a three-phase resistance permanently connected to the slip rings. Shunt contactors of the double-pole type (where sizes permit) are used to short circuit successive portions of the resistance as the motor accelerates. The energizing current is obtained from a potential transformer in the primary circuit between the oil switch and the motor. Current limit relays govern the rate of acceleration. In case the primary oil switch is opened intentionally, or by means of the no-voltage release, the secondary contactors open, automatically inserting the entire resistance in the secondary circuit so that, even with the master controller still in the running position, the motor will receive no harm when the voltage is again thrown on the line. This automatic action of the secondary contactors also affords protection against reversing with the resistance all cut out, since the contactors drop out as the oil switch is opened and latch again as it is thrown to the reverse position.

CONTROLLER FOR AC MOTOR OPERATING AT TWO SPEEDS

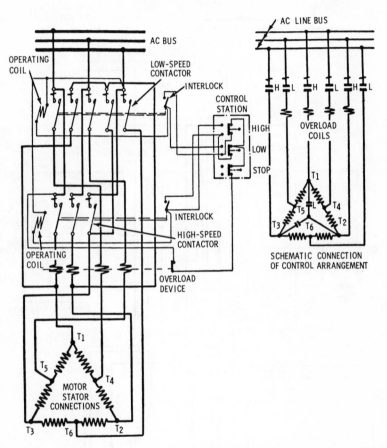

Operation—Generally the purpose of controllers for motors having more than one speed is to interconnect the stator terminals in a desirable manner and also to connect them to the line as required for each speed. In the system of control under consideration, the schematic diagram shows the basic principles. Here for the sake of clarity the high-speed and low-speed contacts are labeled "H" and "L" respectively.

With reference to the complete diagram, one button is utilized for each speed. If it is desired to change the speed from low to high for example, the operation of the high-speed button will automatically cause the motor to change over to that speed.

CONTROLLER FOR AC MULTISPEED MOTOR

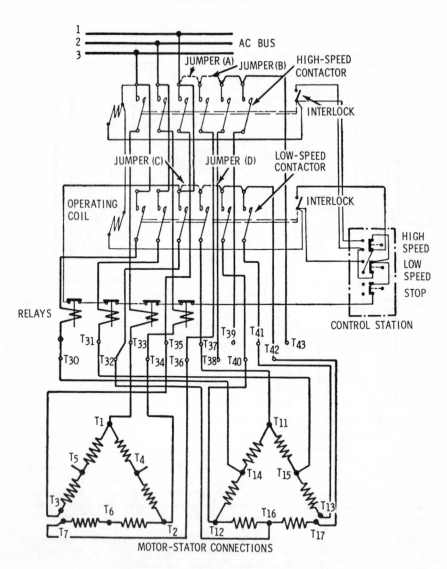

MOTOR-STATOR CONNECTIONS

Note—For operating data see following page.

CONNECTION DATA FOR MULTISPEED AC MOTOR

SPEEDS	OMIT JUMPERS	CONNECT TERMINALS AS FOLLOWS
600/900	a and c	T_1-T_{37}, T_2-T_{40}, T_3-T_{41}, T_4-T_{30}, T_5-T_{31}, T_6-T_{32}, T_7-T_{42}, T_{11}-T_{36}, T_{12}-T_{38}, T_{14}-T_{33}, T_{15}-T_{34}, T_{16}-T_{35}, T_{17}-T_{43}
600/1200	b and c	T_1-T_{33}-T_{37}, T_2-T_{34}-T_{40}, T_3-T_{35}-T_{41}, T_4-T_{30}, T_5-T_{31}, T_6-T_{32}, T_7-T_{36}-T_{42}
600/1800	b and c	T_1-T_{37}, T_2-T_{40}, T_3-T_{41}, T_4-T_{30}, T_5-T_{31}, T_6-T_{32}, T_7-T_{42}, T_{11}-T_{33}, T_{12}-T_{34}, T_{13}-T_{35}, T_{17}-T_{36}
900/1200	b and c	T_1-T_{33}, T_2-T_{34}, T_3-T_{35}, T_{12}-T_{40}, T_{13}-T_{41}, T_{14}-T_{30}, T_{15}-T_{31}, T_{16}-T_{32}, T_{17}-T_{42}
900/1800	b and c	T_{11}-T_{33}-T_{37}, T_{12}-T_{34}-T_{40}, T_{13}-T_{35}-T_{41}, T_{14}-T_{30}, T_{15}-T_{31}, T_{16}-T_{32}, T_{17}-T_{36}-T_{42}
1200/1800	b and d	T_1-T_{30}, T_2-T_{31}, T_3-T_{32}, T_7-T_{37}, T_{11}-T_{33}, T_{12}-T_{34}, T_{13}-T_{35}, T_{17}-T_{36}

Operation—In the connection diagram shown on the previous page, the 4-speed motor is connected for two speeds; that is, when the low-speed button is operated, three of the contacts connect the winding parallel-star and the other three connect the winding to the line.

This gives eight poles or a synchronous speed of $\dfrac{120 \times 60}{8}$ or 900 r.p.m.

Again when the high-speed button is operated, the low-speed contacts open and the delta connection is completed, connecting the winding to the line through six poles which give a synchronous speed of $\dfrac{120 \times 60}{6}$ or 1200 r.p.m.

Method of connection to obtain 4 speeds is shown in the accompanying table.

MOTOR-CONTROL METHODS

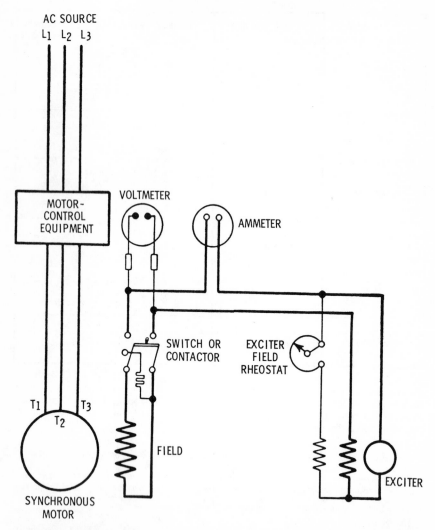

Simplified Diagram Showing Method of Exciter Connection to Synchronous Motor—This type of motor is usually provided with a damper winding on the pole faces which permits it to be started as an induction motor. The DC field winding is then energized at or near synchronous speed to pull the motor into step.

MOTOR-CONTROL METHODS

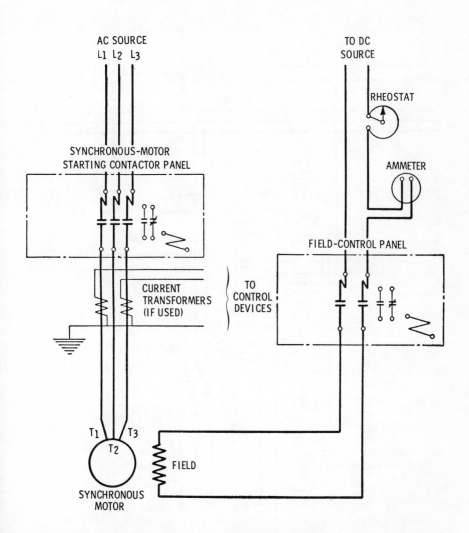

Main Circuit Wiring for Across-the-Line Synchronous Motor Starter—Depending upon the control method used, the starting contactor panel may contain several relays, and if remotely controlled, the starting equipment will in addition have provisions for the start and stop push-button station.

MOTOR-CONTROL METHODS

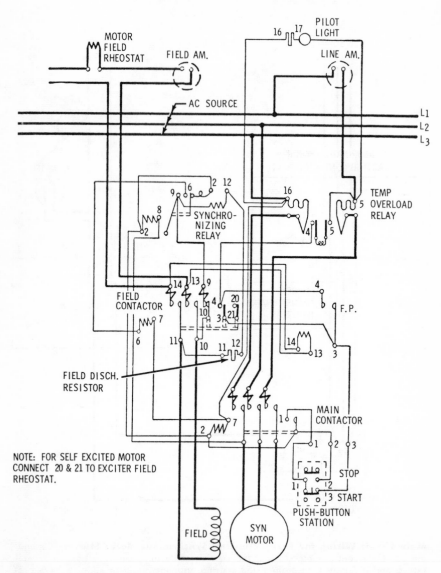

Wiring of a Typical Automatic, Across-the-Line, Synchronous Motor Starter.

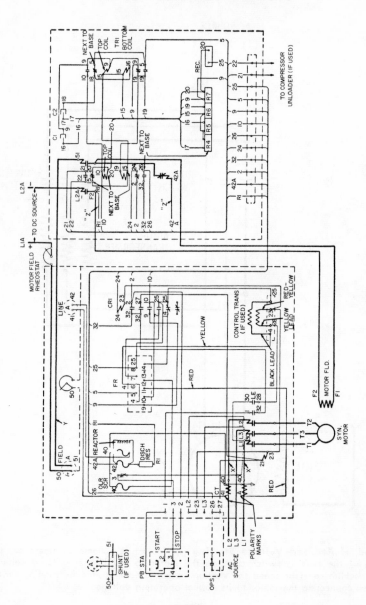

Diagram of General Electric Across-the-Line Synchronous Motor, Low-Voltage Magnetic Starter.

MOTOR-CONTROL METHODS

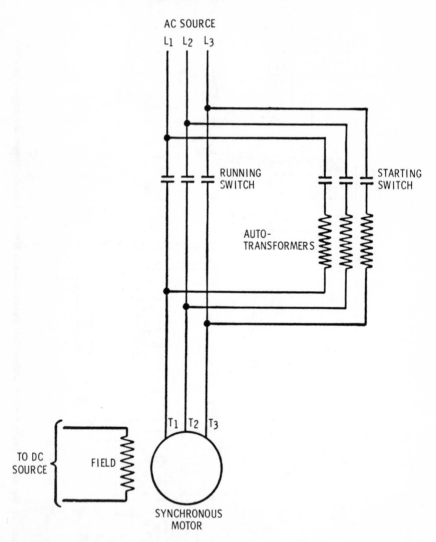

AC SOURCE

L₁ L₂ L₃

RUNNING
SWITCH

STARTING
SWITCH

AUTO-
TRANSFORMERS

T₁ T₂ T₃

TO DC
SOURCE

FIELD

SYNCHRONOUS
MOTOR

Method of Reduced Voltage Starting—In a starting scheme of this type, the closing of the starting switch connects the motor to the line at reduced voltage. After reaching constant speed the starting switch is opened and the running switch is closed connecting the motor to its normal operating voltage.

MOTOR-CONTROL METHODS

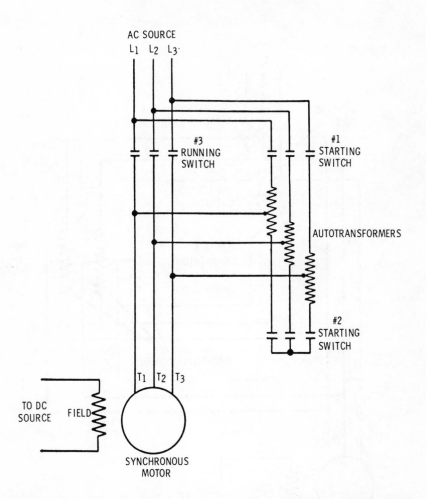

Method of Reduced Voltage Starting Using Three Switches or Contactors—In this starting method, switches #1 and #2 are first closed simultaneously connecting the motor to the line through the star-connected autotransformers. Power is then supplied to the motor at reduced voltage. Switch #1 is opened as soon as the speed becomes constant and switch #3 closes instantly, being electrically interlocked with switch #1. This connects the motor directly across the line, the terminal voltage having increased to normal without dropping to zero.

MOTOR-CONTROL METHODS

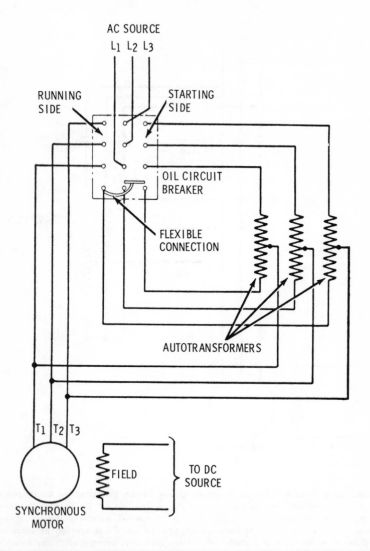

AC SOURCE
L_1 L_2 L_3

RUNNING
SIDE

STARTING
SIDE

OIL CIRCUIT
BREAKER

FLEXIBLE
CONNECTION

AUTOTRANSFORMERS

T_1 T_2 T_3

FIELD

TO DC
SOURCE

SYNCHRONOUS
MOTOR

Method of Reduced Voltage Starting of Synchronous Motor Using a Double-Throw Oil Circuit Breaker and Three Autotransformers.

MOTOR-CONTROL METHODS

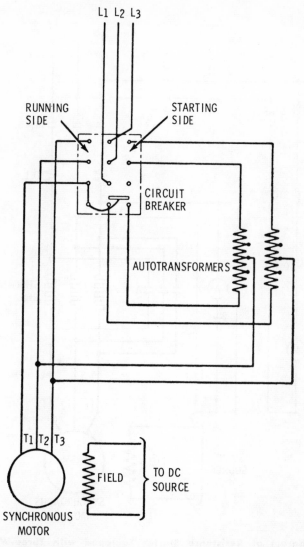

Reduced Voltage Starting Using a Double-Throw Oil Circuit Breaker and Two Autotransformers.

MOTOR-CONTROL METHODS

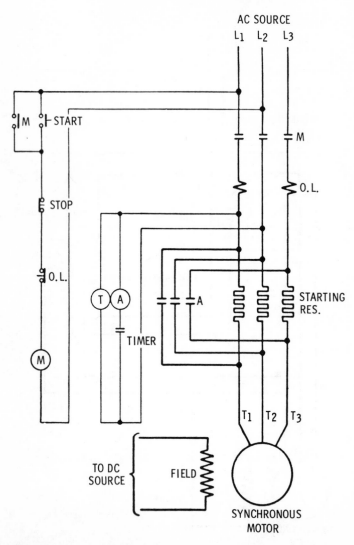

Wiring Diagram of Resistance Starter Equipped with Three-Wire Push Buttons Which Includes Low-Voltage Protection—In the diagram M represents main running contactor, OL, overload relays A, starting contactor and T timing relay.

MOTOR-CONTROL METHODS

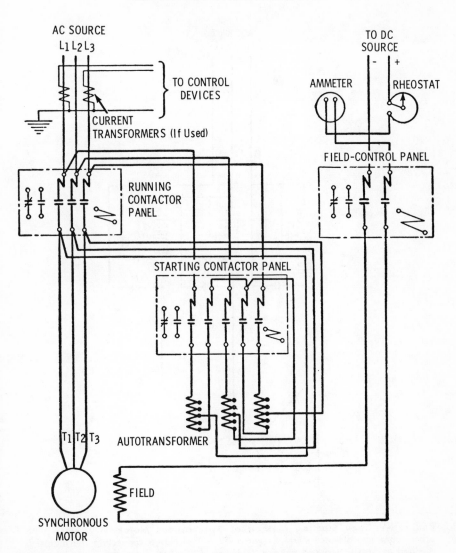

Main Connections for Synchronous Motor Reduced-Voltage Starter—Depending upon the size of the motor and the control scheme used, the complete control wiring may consist of three separate panels as illustrated.

281

MOTOR-CONTROL METHODS

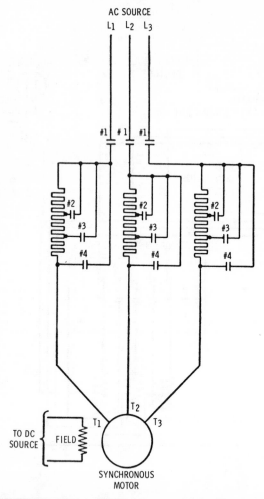

Reduced-Voltage Starting Method of Synchronous Motor—In common with other types of resistance starters, switch #1 is first closed connecting the motor to the line at greatly reduced voltage. Switches #2, 3 and 4 are then closed in turn usually by means of timing devices, providing a step-by-step reduction in resistance until finally only switches #1 and #4 will remain closed, thus providing full voltage to the motor terminals.

MOTOR-CONTROL METHODS

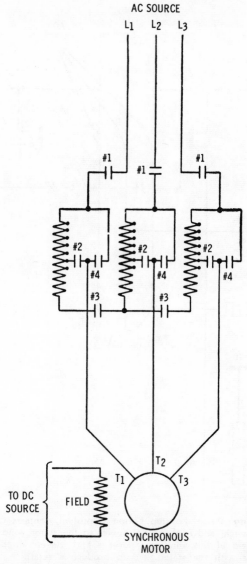

AC SOURCE

Wiring Diagram Showing Korndorfer Method of Reduced-Voltage Starting.

MOTOR-CONTROL METHODS

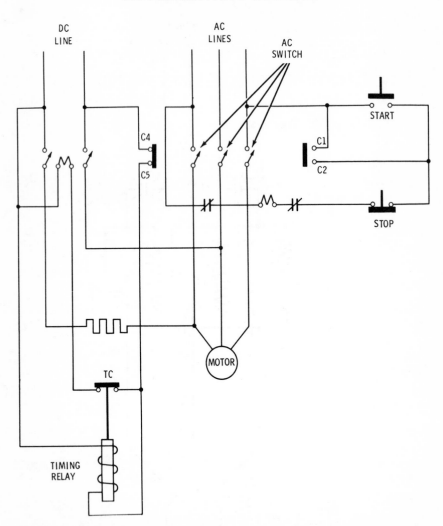

Dynamic Braking—When the stop button is pushed, contacts C4-C5 close, energizing the DC switch, and applying DC power to the stator winding of the motor. The stationary field of this winding induces a high current in the rotor bars. The rotor field reacts with the stator field to produce a retarding torque that stops the motor.

MISCELLANEOUS
WIRING
DIAGRAMS

CURRENT-DIFFERENTIAL PROTECTION

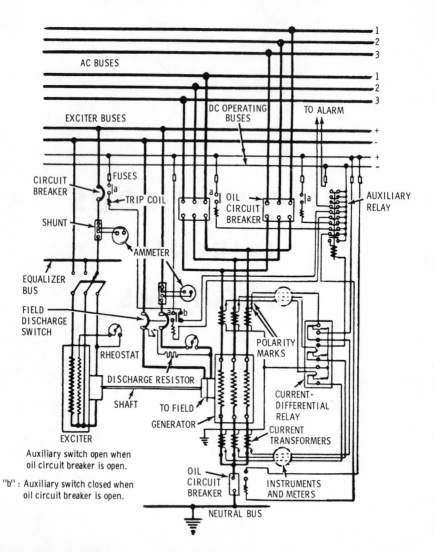

Complete Diagram of Connections for Current-Differential Protection of Three-Phase, Star-Connected, Alternating-Current Generator with Grounded Neutral and Direct-Current Exciter.

CURRENT-DIFFERENTIAL PROTECTION

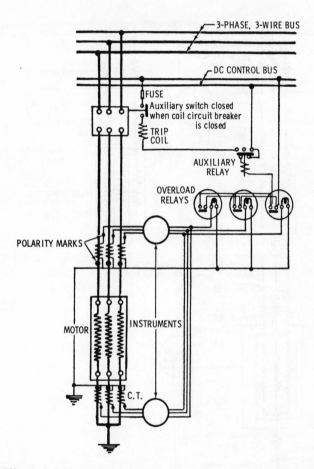

Current-Differential Protection of Station Auxiliary Feeder Using Induction-Type Overload Relays.

Current-differential protection consists essentially of current transformers installed at each end of the generator windings with their secondaries connected in series and relays connected differentially so that their functioning depends upon a difference of current flowing through the two sets of current transformers.

It is obvious that the differential protection disconnects the machine only in the case of electrical failure in the machine or its connecting leads.

DIFFERENTIAL PROTECTION

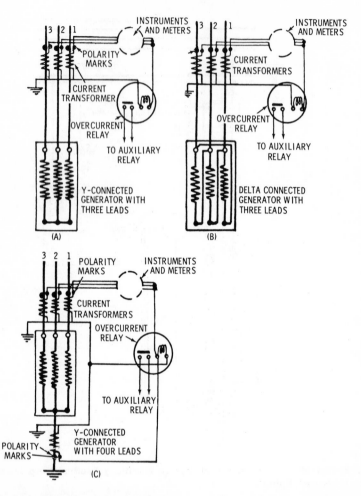

Method of obtaining differential protection when such provision was not made in the manufacture of the machine (where the phase leads were not brought out). Figs. A, B, and C show the connection used as expedients in such cases. Fig. A shows current differential protection of a three-phase, Y-connection, AC generator, neutral not brought out. Fig. B Current-differential protection of a three-phase, delta-connected, AC generator, phase leads not brought out. Fig. C Current-differential protection of a three-phase, Y-connected, AC generator, neutral only brought out.

CURRENT-DIFFERENTIAL PROTECTION

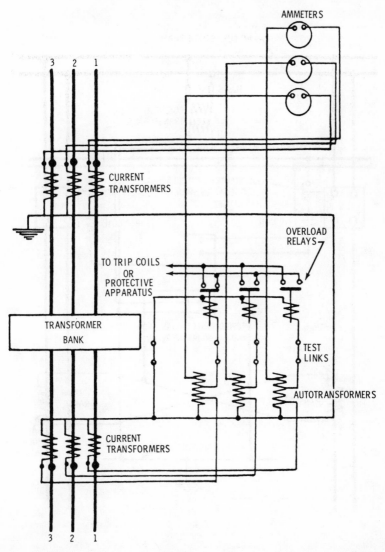

Current-Differential Protection Over a Transformer Bank Showing Application of Test-Links Facilitating Testing of Relay Coils.

BALANCED-POWER PROTECTION

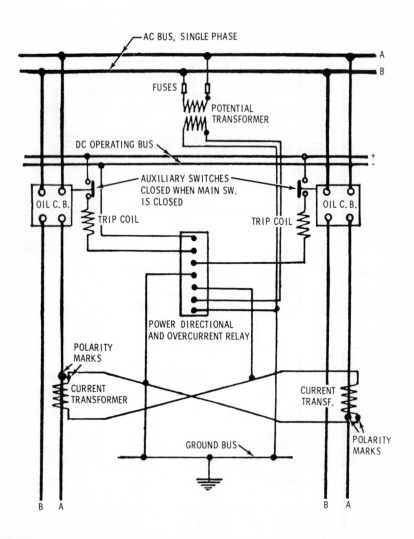

Balanced Power Connection for Two Parallel Incoming, Outgoing or Tie Lines, Single-Phase DC Current Used for Tripping Oil Circuit Breakers.

BALANCED AND OVERCURRENT PROTECTION

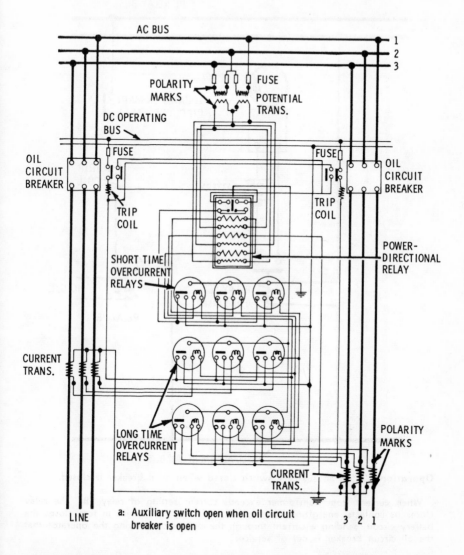

Separate Balanced and Overcurrent Protection for Two Parallel Three-Phase Incoming, Outgoing or Tie Lines with Grounded Neutral.

BELL-ALARM CONNECTIONS

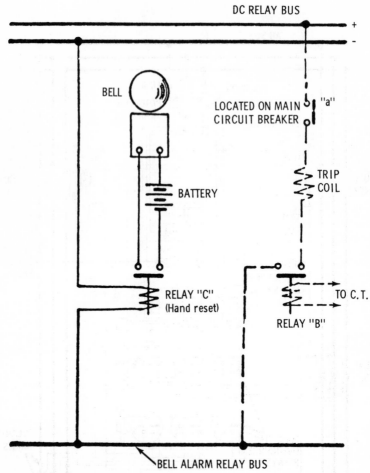

Operation—"A" is an auxiliary switch closed when main breaker is closed.

When current from transformer exceeds current setting of relay "B," the relay closes its contacts, energizing the trip coil and relay "C" which in turn closes the battery circuit, sending a current through the bell, and notifying the operator that the oil circuit breaker is out of service.

Note, that relay "C" is usually hand reset, and is reset for service by the attendant.

EMERGENCY SWITCHING METHODS

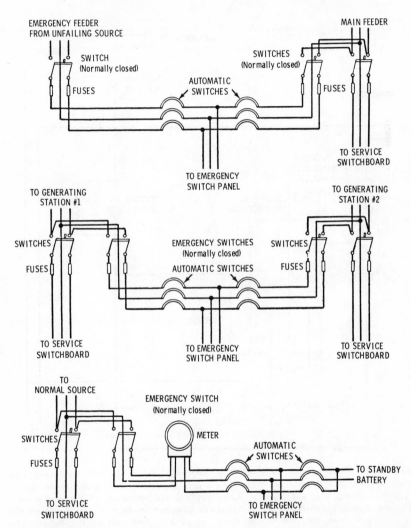

Operation—The above diagrams represent emergency switching methods generally utilized in public institutions such as hospitals, schools, etc. where it is imperative that an unfailing lighting source be available. The automatic switches shown will automatically close themselves when the normal supply fails, causing the service to remain uninterrupted.

TYPICAL CARBON-ARC SEARCHLIGHT

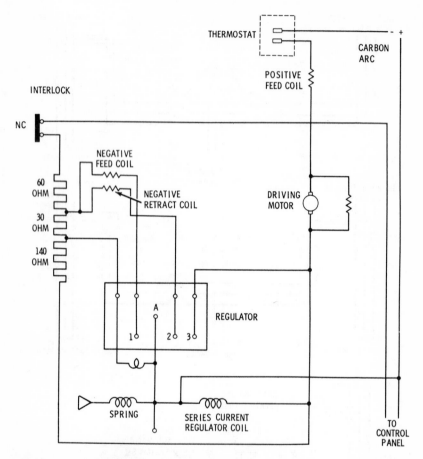

Carbon-Arc Searchlight Control—The negative carbon is fed backward and forward to control the current through the arc. The movement is controlled by an adjustable spring and a regulator. When the light is operating at the proper current, the movable contact A is held midway between contacts 1 and 2. When the arc current is low, the pull of the spring is greater than that of the current coil and contact A is pulled against contact 1. This action places voltage from taps 1 and 2 of the resistor across the negative feed coil. When the current is high, the pull of the coil exceeds that of the spring and contact A is pulled against contact 2. This action places voltage from taps 1 and 2 of the resistor across the negative retract coil.

VARIOUS SWITCHING METHODS

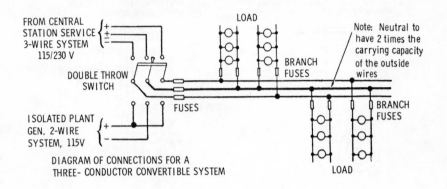

FROM CENTRAL
STATION SERVICE
3-WIRE SYSTEM
115/230 V

LOAD

Note: Neutral to
have 2 times the
carrying capacity
of the outside
wires

BRANCH
FUSES

DOUBLE THROW
SWITCH

FUSES

ISOLATED PLANT
GEN. 2-WIRE
SYSTEM, 115V

BRANCH
FUSES

LOAD

DIAGRAM OF CONNECTIONS FOR A
THREE- CONDUCTOR CONVERTIBLE SYSTEM

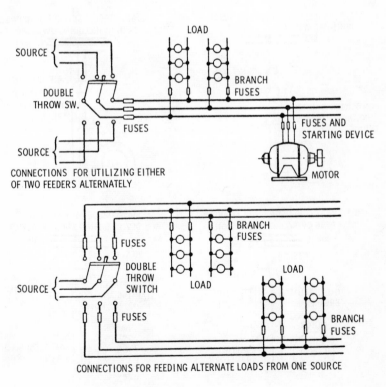

SOURCE

LOAD

DOUBLE
THROW SW.

BRANCH
FUSES

FUSES

FUSES AND
STARTING DEVICE

SOURCE

MOTOR

CONNECTIONS FOR UTILIZING EITHER
OF TWO FEEDERS ALTERNATELY

FUSES

BRANCH
FUSES

DOUBLE
THROW
SWITCH

LOAD

LOAD

SOURCE

FUSES

BRANCH
FUSES

CONNECTIONS FOR FEEDING ALTERNATE LOADS FROM ONE SOURCE

MOTOR DISCONNECTING AND CONTROL METHODS

DISCONNECTING METHOD FOR SMALL
STATIONARY MOTOR

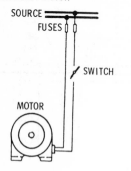

SOURCE
FUSES

SWITCH

MOTOR

DISCONNECTING METHOD FOR
STATIONARY MOTOR

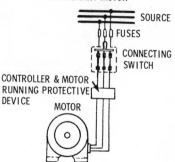

SOURCE

FUSES

CONNECTING
SWITCH

CONTROLLER & MOTOR
RUNNING PROTECTIVE
DEVICE

MOTOR

DISCONNECTING METHOD FOR SMALL
PORTABLE MOTOR

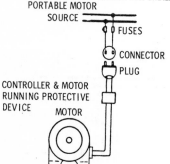

SOURCE

FUSES

CONNECTOR

PLUG

CONTROLLER & MOTOR
RUNNING PROTECTIVE
DEVICE

MOTOR

AIR CIRCUIT BREAKER DISCONNECTING
METHOD INCLUDING OVERLOAD DEVICE

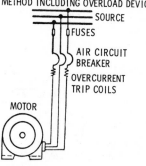

SOURCE

FUSES

AIR CIRCUIT
BREAKER

OVERCURRENT
TRIP COILS

MOTOR

DISCONNECTING METHOD FOR AC MOTOR
INCLUDING OVERCURRENT TRIP COILS

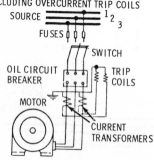

SOURCE   1
            2
              3
FUSES

SWITCH

OIL CIRCUIT
BREAKER

TRIP
COILS

MOTOR

CURRENT
TRANSFORMERS

SHUNTING OUT OF PROTECTIVE
DEVICE DURING STARTING PERIOD

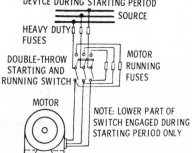

SOURCE

HEAVY DUTY
FUSES

DOUBLE-THROW
STARTING AND
RUNNING SWITCH

MOTOR
RUNNING
FUSES

MOTOR

NOTE: LOWER PART OF
SWITCH ENGAGED DURING
STARTING PERIOD ONLY

POWER DISTRIBUTION AND WIRING METHODS

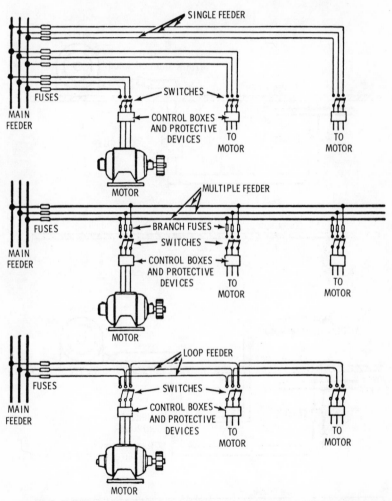

The above diagrams suggest three methods of motor wiring. However, due to individual operating conditions, the type of wiring adopted should be carefully analyzed for the particular case involved. Certain applications, for example, by their very nature will prove themselves better suited for one scheme than the other. The National Electric Code as well as any local requirements should be strictly adhered to and the wire should be of ample capacity to prevent excessive voltage drops.

REMOTE-CONTROL WIRING FOR SMALL MOTORS

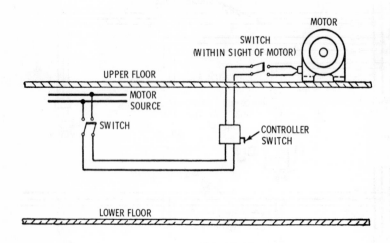

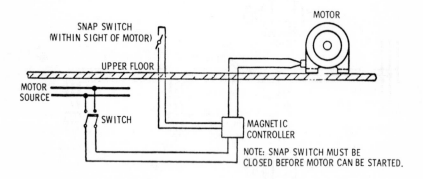

Note—All motors and control wiring should be carefully installed in accordance with the National Electric Code and any local requirement. The wire should be of ample capacity based on a maximum drop of 2 per cent of line voltage at full load current.

HEATING ELEMENTS ON THREE-PHASE SYSTEMS

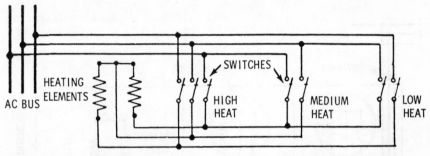

Method of Connecting Heating Elements for Various Degrees of Heat.

To prevent excessive voltage drop in load systems containing heating elements, several load-balancing switches may be utilized as shown. Maximum heating is provided when switches marked HIGH HEAT are closed. This is due to the fact that in this position of the switches both heating elements receive the maximum voltage.

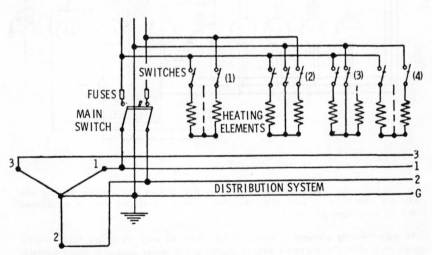

Switching Methods for Electric Heating Range.

When an electric heating range is connected as shown, the heat is regulated by connecting the heating element in various ways, depending upon the amount of heat required.

DIAGRAM OF CONNECTION FOR ELECTRIC RANGE

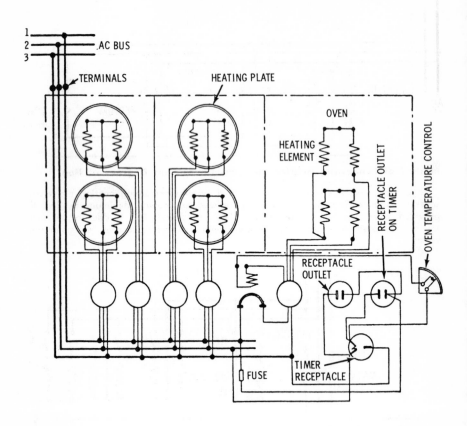

In a standard type of electric range such as that shown, the various heating elements are connected in such a manner that a nearly balanced load is established under all conditions of usage.

As each heating element is rated at less than 30 amp. each, no fuses are required to protect the elements and their connecting wires except in the receptacle circuit, where an exterior appliance may be connected.

The wiring should be of an approved and sufficient size to supply the range at its rated wattage without overheating. Generally for a range rated at 7500 watts, #8 wire is required.

SWITCHING PANELS AND FEEDER
DISTRIBUTION METHODS

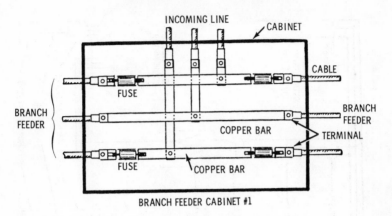

BRANCH FEEDER CABINET #1

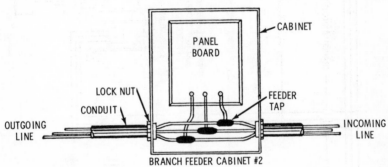

BRANCH FEEDER CABINET #2

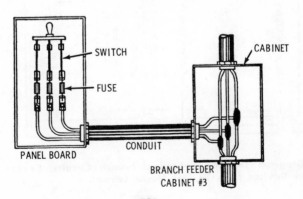

MOTOR-CONTROL METHODS

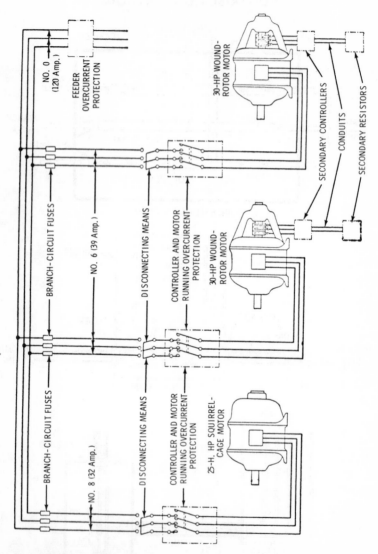

Wiring Diagram Showing Individual Branch Circuits, Feeder Circuit and Protective Devices in a Typical Motor Layout.

AUTOMATIC ELECTRIC WATER HEATERS

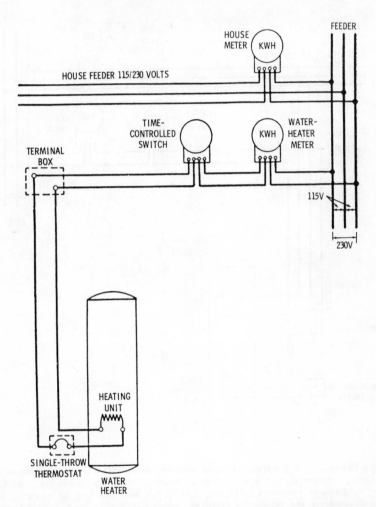

Wiring Diagram for Limited-Demand Service on a Single-Unit Water Heater
—In a circuit of this type, the single-throw, single-pole thermostat functions to close and open the circuit to the heating unit at specified temperatures according to its setting. The time-controlled switch will determine the hours of the day when the circuit will be opened or closed, thus preventing unlimited use of hot water during the hours of greatest power load.

AUTOMATIC ELECTRIC WATER HEATERS

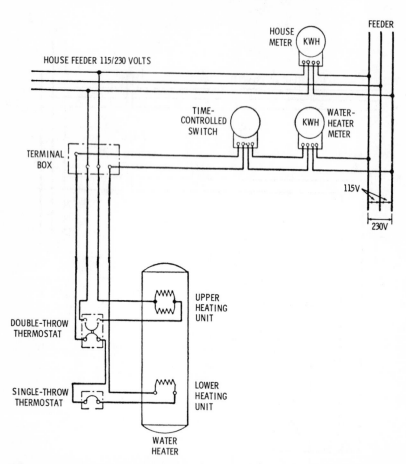

Wiring Diagram for Limited-Demand Service on Double-Unit Water Heater—
In a wiring method of this type, the upper heating unit is controlled by a double-throw, single-pole, thermostatic switch. This switch has two sets of contacts, one of which controls the flow of current to the upper heating unit and the other controls the flow of current to the lower thermostat. The lower heating unit is controlled by a single-throw, single-pole, thermostatic switch. This switch has only one set of contacts and opens and closes in response to the temperature of the water in the lower tank. The function of the time switch is to prevent unlimited use of hot water during a predetermined time (or times), usually during that period of the day when the general demand for power is the greatest.

REVERSING DRUM SWITCH

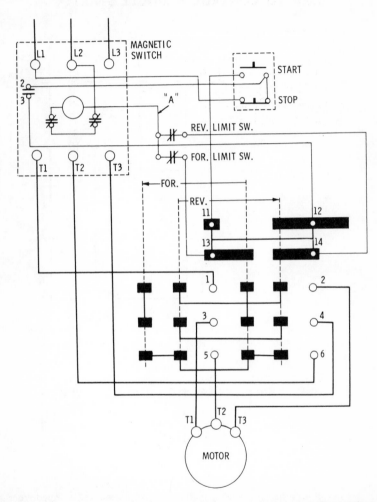

The reversing drum switch shown provides no-voltage protection when the drum switch is used with a full-voltage starter and a start-stop push button station. The starting contact of the interlock is open when the drum switch handle is in either the forward or reverse position and closed when the handle is in the off position. If a voltage failure occurs while the handle is in either position, the starter will not reclose when voltage returns because of the open interlock contact. The handle must be returned to the off position and the start button pressed.

MORE THAN ONE START-STOP STATION
USED TO CONTROL A SINGLE STARTER

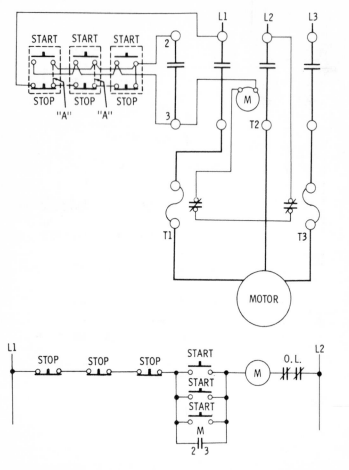

This is a useful arrangement when a motor must be started and stopped from any of several widely separated locations.

Notice that it would also be possible to use only one start-stop station and have several stop buttons at different locations to serve as emergency stops.

If start-stop stations are provided with the connections "A" shown in the diagram, this connection must be removed from all but one of the start-stop stations used.

STEP-DOWN TRANSFORMER IN CONTROL CIRCUIT

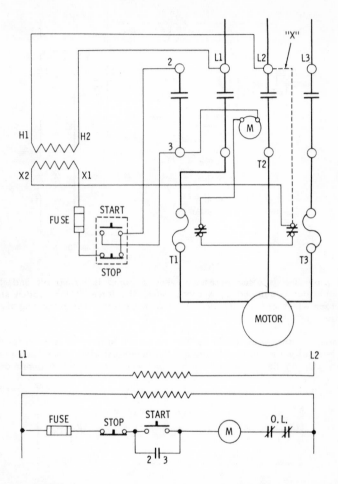

Step-Down Transformer Provides Low Voltage for Control Circuit Wired for Three-Wire Control—The starter coil is to be operated on a voltage lower than line voltage. (Usually done for safety reasons.) This requires the use of a step-down transformer in the pilot circuit. The starter is operated from a start-stop push-button station.

When a control circuit step-down transformer is used with some starters, the wiring connection "X" must be removed. Note that a fuse is added to the transformer secondary.

PUMP OPERATION

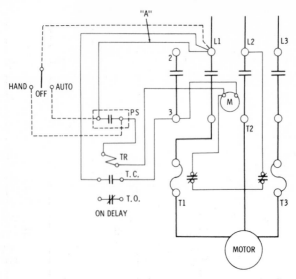

Surge protection is often necessary when a pump is turned off and the long column of water is stopped by a check valve. The force of the sudden stop may cause surges which operate the pressure switch contacts, thus subjecting the starter to "chattering."

"Backspin" is the name given to the backward turning of a centrifugal pump when a head of water runs back through the pump just after it has been turned off. Obviously starting the pump during backspin might damage the pump or motor.

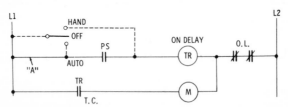

System Provides Backspin Protection and Surge Protection on Stopping—
The pressure switch energizes the timer (TR), but the motor cannot start until the time-delay contact has closed. The timer can thus be set for a time long enough to allow all surges and backspin to stop.

The dotted lines show how a selector switch can be added to by-pass the pressure switch if necessary. This is often used for motor testing purposes. It does not eliminate the time delay however. If the selector switch is added, the wire "A" must be removed.

PUMP OPERATION

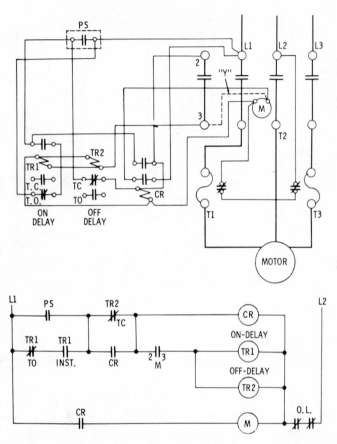

System Provides Surge Protection on Both Starting and Stopping. Backspin Protection Automatically Included—Two timing relays are used here, one to provide surge protection on starting and one to provide surge protection on stopping and backspin protection. TR1 is an "on-delay" timer used for surge protection on starting. When the pressure switch contact closes, relay CR, the starter and the two timers are energized. The instantaneous contact on TR1 closes, by-passing the pressure switch contact and preventing the pump motor starter from dropping out even though starting surges open the pressure contact. After the timing period, the time delay contact of TR1 opens the by-pass and PS can then stop the pump at the proper pressure. TR2 is an "off-delay" timer for surge protection on stopping and backspin protection. Once turned off, the system cannot be operated again until timer TR2 has timed out and its normally closed contact is closed.

SEQUENCE CONTROL

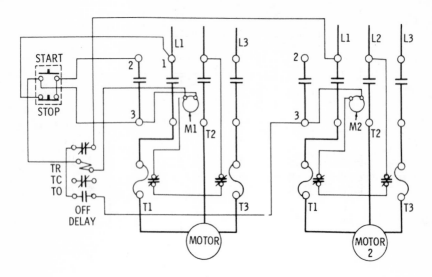

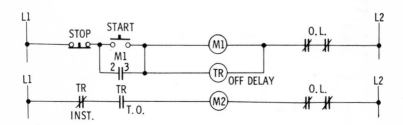

Sequence Control of Two Motors—One to Start and Run for a Short Time After the Other Stops—In this system it is desired to have a second motor started automatically when the first is stopped. The second motor is to run only for a given length of time. Such an application might be found where the second motor is needed to run a cooling fan or a pump.

To accomplish this an off-delay timer (TR) is used. When the start button is pressed, it energizes both M1 and TR. The operation of TR closes its time-delay contact but the circuit to M2 is kept open by the opening of the instantaneous contact. As soon as the stop button is pressed, both M1 and TR are dropped out. This closes the instantaneous contact on TR and starts M2. M2 will continue to run until TR times out and the time delay contact opens.

PUSH-BUTTON STATION WIRING

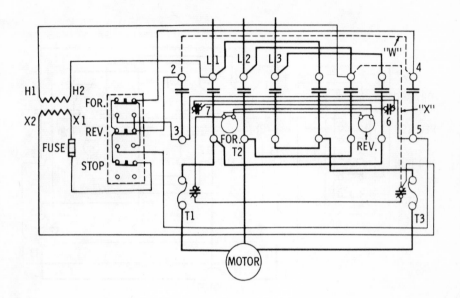

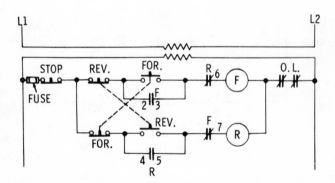

Push Button Wired So Starter Can Be Switched from One Direction to the Other Without Pushing Stop Button—This scheme allows immediate reversal of the motor when it is running in either direction. With some reversing switches wire "W" may have to be removed. The diagram shows the control circuit set up for reduced voltage control, although this may not be necessary in many cases. Notice that wire "X" must be removed when reduced voltage control is used.

JOGGING

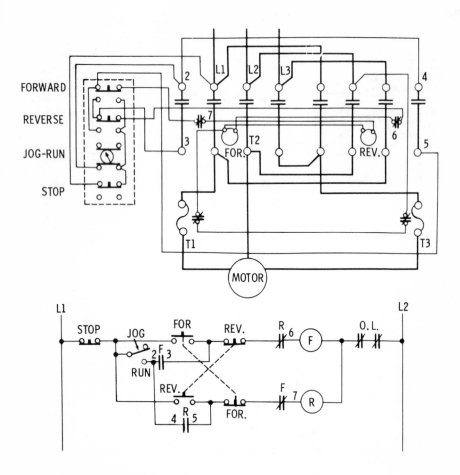

Starting, Stopping and Jogging in Either Direction. Jogging Controlled Through a Jogging Selector Switch—Here, the motor can run normally in either direction or can be jogged in either direction. With the selector in the run position, the motor can be started in either direction and will stop when the stop button is pressed. It is not necessary to press the stop button before changing from forward to reverse. With the selector in the jog position, the forward and reverse buttons act as jogging buttons. The motor will run in the indicated direction when one of them is pressed but will stop as soon as the button is released.

AUDEL BOOKS *practical reading for profit*

Automobile Guide   (AUD-1)

Practical reference for auto mechanics, servicemen, trainees & owners. Explains theory, construction and servicing of modern domestic motor cars. FEATURES: All parts of an automobile—engines—pistons—rings—connecting rods—crankshafts—valves—cams—timing—cooling systems—fuel-feed systems—carburetors—automatic choke—transmissions—clutches—universals—propeller shafts—differentials—rear axles—running gear—brakes—wheel alignment—steering gear—tires—lubrication—ignition systems—generators—starters—lighting systems— **$6⁹⁵** storage batteries.

Home Appliance Servicing   (AUD-2)

A practical "How To Do It" book for electric & gas servicemen, mechanics & dealers. Covers principles, servicing and repairing of home appliances. Tells how to locate troubles, make repairs, reassemble and connect, wiring diagrams and testing methods. Tells how to fix electric refrigerators, washers, ranges, toasters, ironers, broilers, dryers, vacuums, fans, and **$6⁹⁵** other appliances.

Radiomans Guide   (AUD-3A)

A key to the practical understanding of radio. For radio engineers, servicemen, amateurs. FEATURES: Radio fundamentals and Ohm's law—physics of sound as related to radio—radio-wave transmission—electrical measuring instruments—power supply units—resistors, inductors and capacitors—radio transformers—vacuum tubes—radio receivers—speakers—antenna **$5** systems—radio testing.

Television Service Manual   (AUD-3B)

Now completely updated and revised to include the latest designs and information. Thoroughly covers television with transmitter theory, antenna designs, receiver circuit operation and the picture tube. Provides the practical information necessary for accurate diagnosis and repair of both black-and-white and color television receivers. A MUST BOOK FOR ANYONE **$5** IN TELEVISION.

Handy Book of Practical Electricity   (AUD-4)

For maintenance engineers, electricians and all electrical workers. A ready reference book, giving complete instruction and practical information on the rules and laws of electricity—maintenance of electrical machinery—AC and DC motors—wiring diagrams—house lighting—power wiring—meter and instrument connections—bells and signal wiring—motor wiring—transformer connections—fractional-horsepower motors—circuit breakers—relay protection—switchgear—power stations—automatic substations. THE KEY TO A PRACTICAL **$5⁹⁵** UNDERSTANDING OF ELECTRICITY.

Truck & Tractor Guide   (AUD-5)

A shop companion for truck mechanics and drivers—shop foremen—garagemen—maintenance men—helpers—owners—troubleshooters—fleet maintenance men—bus mechanics and drivers—farm tractor operators and mechanics. Covers gas and diesel motor principles—construction—operation—maintenance—repair—service operations—troubleshooting—engine tune-up—carburetor adjusting—ignition tuning—brakes—service of all parts.—1001 FACTS AT YOUR **$5⁹⁵** FINGER TIPS.

Plumbers and Pipe Fitters Library—3 Vols.   (AUD-6)

New revised edition. A practical illustrated trade assistant and reference for master plumbers, journeyman and apprentice pipe fitters, gas fitters and helpers, builders, contractors, and engineers. Explains in simple language, illustrations, diagrams, charts, graphs and pictures, the principles of modern plumbing and pipe-fitting practices.
Vol. 1—Materials, tools, calculations.
Vol. 2—Drainage, fittings, fixtures.   **$9⁹⁵**
Vol. 3—Installation, heating, welding. $3.50 a volume.

Painting & Decorating Manual (AUD-7)

A reliable guide for painters, journeymen, apprentices, contractors, home owners, and all paint users. The book is divided into two sections. Section I contains information on: basic tools and equipment; selection of paint; guide to color; techniques of applying paint with brush, roller and spray gun; wood and floor finishing. Section II provides information about: cost estimate; glossary of terms; a review of the mathematics and information about **$4**⁹⁵ running a paint business. Profusely illustrated.

Carpenters & Builders Guides—4 Vols. (AUD-8)

A practical illustrated trade assistant on modern construction for carpenters, builders, and all woodworkers. Explains in practical, concise language and illustrations all the principles, advances and short cuts based on modern practice. How to calculate various jobs.
Vol.1—Tools, steel square, saw filing, joinery, cabinets.
Vol. 2—Mathematics, plans, specifications, estimates.
Vol. 3—House and roof framing, laying out, foundations.
Vol. 4—Doors, windows, stairs, millwork, painting. $4.95 a volume.   **$16**⁹⁵

Diesel Engine Manual (AUD-9)

A practical treatise on the theory, operation and maintenance of modern Diesel engines. Explains Diesel principles—valves—timing—fuel pumps—pistons and rings—cylinders—lubrication—cooling system—fuel oil—engine indicator—governors—engine reversing—answers on operation—calculations. AN IMPORTANT GUIDE FOR ENGINEERS, OPERATORS, **$6** STUDENTS.

Welders Guide (AUD-10)

A concise, practical text on operation and maintenance of all welding machines, for all mechanics. Covers electric, oxyacetylene, thermit, unionmelt welding for sheet metal; spot and pipe welds; pressure vessels; aluminum, copper, brass, bronze and other metals; airplane work; surface hardening and hard facing; cutting; brazing; eye protection. EVERY **$4**⁹⁵ WELDER SHOULD OWN THIS GUIDE.

Mathematics & Calculations for Mechanics (AUD-11)

Mathematics for home study or shop reference. This work has been arranged as a progressive study, starting with the first principles of arithmetic and advancing step-by-step, through the various phases of mathematics. Thousands of mathematical calculations and tables. New, easy, correct methods covering a complete review of practical arithmetic. Illustrated **$4**⁹⁵ with examples. A REAL HELP TO ALL MECHANICS.

Machinists Library (AUD-12)

Covers modern machine-shop practice. Tells how to set up and operate lathes, screw and milling machines, shapers, drill presses and all other machine tools. A complete reference library. A SHOP COMPANION THAT ANSWERS YOUR QUESTIONS.
Vol. 1—Basic Machine Shop Practices.
Vol. 2—Machine Shop.
Vol. 3—Toolmakers Handy Book. $4.95 a volume.   **$13**⁵⁰

Wiring Diagrams for Light & Power (AUD-13)

Brand-new updated edition. Electricians, wiremen, linemen, plant superintendents, construction engineers, electrical contractors and students will find these diagrams a valuable source of practical help. Each diagram is complete and self-explaining. A PRACTICAL **$4** HANDY BOOK OF ELECTRICAL HOOK-UPS.

Home Refrigeration and Air Conditioning (AUD-14A)

NEW AND UP-TO-DATE. Covers basic principles, servicing, operation, and repair of modern household refrigerators and air conditioners. Automobile air conditioners are also included. Troubleshooting charts aid in trouble diagnosis. **A gold mine of essential facts** **$6**⁹⁵ **for engineers, servicemen, and users.**

Commercial Refrigeration   (AUD-14B)

Installation, operation, and repair of commercial refrigeration systems. Included are ice-making plants, locker plants, grocery and supermarket refrigerated display cases, etc. Trouble charts aid in the diagnosis and repair of defective systems. **$5**⁹⁵

New Electric Library—10 Vols.   (AUD-15A)

For engineers, electricians, electrical workers, mechanics and students. Presenting in simple, concise form the fundamental principles, rules and applications of applied electricity. Fully illustrated with diagrams and sketches, also calculations and tables for ready reference. Based on the best knowledge and experience of applied electricity.

Vol. 1 (AUD-15)—Electricity, magnetism, armature winding, repairs.
Vol. 2 (AUD-16)—Dynamos, DC motors, construction, installation, maintenance, troubleshooting.
Vol. 3 (AUD-17)—Electrical testing instruments, storage battery construction and repairs.
Vol. 4 (AUD-18)—Alternating current principles and diagrams, power factor, alternators, transformers.
Vol. 5 (AUD-19)—AC motors, converters, switches, fuses, circuit breakers.
Vol. 6 (AUD-20)—Relays, capacitors, regulators, rectifiers, meters, switchboards, power-station practice.
Vol. 7 (AUD-21)—Wiring, high-tension transmission, plans, calculations.
Vol. 8 (AUD-22)—Railways, signals, elevators.
Vol. 9 (AUD-23)—Radio, telephone, telegraph, television, motion pictures.
Vol. 10 (AUD-24)—Refrigeration, illumination, welding, X-ray, modern electrical appliances.

$3.00 a volume   COMPLETE SET **$25**

Answers on Blueprint Reading   (AUD-25)

Covers all types of blueprint reading for mechanics and builders. The man who can read blueprints is in line for a better job. This book gives you this secret language, step by step in easy stages. NO OTHER TRADE BOOK LIKE IT. **$4**⁹⁵

Masons & Builders Guides—4 Vols.   (AUD-26)

A practical illustrated trade assistant on modern construction for bricklayers, stone masons, cement workers, plasterers, and tile setters. Explains in clear language and with detailed illustrations all the principles, advances and short cuts based on modern practice—including how to figure and calculate various jobs.

Vol. 1—Brick work, bricklaying, bonding, designs.
Vol. 2—Brick foundations, arches, tile setting, estimates.
Vol. 3—Concrete mixing, placing forms, reinforced stucco.
Vol. 4—Plastering, stone masonry, steel construction, blueprints.   **$10**⁵⁰
$3.00 a volume.

Electric Motors   (AUD-27)

New revised edition. Covers the construction, theory of operation, connection, control, maintenance, and troubleshooting of all types of electric motors. A handy guide for electricians and all electrical workers. **$5**⁹⁵

Oil Burner Guide   (AUD-28)

A practical, concise treatise explaining in detail both domestic and industrial oil burners, including electrical hook-ups and wiring diagrams. Fully covering the theory, construction, installation, operation, testing, servicing and repair of all oil-burner equipment. Fully indexed for quick reference. **$3**⁹⁵

Sheet Metal Pattern Layouts   (AUD-29)

A practical illustrated encyclopedia covering all phases of sheet-metal work including pattern cutting, pattern development and shop procedure. Developed by experts for sheet-metal workers, layout men, mechanics and artisans, apprentices, and students. A MASTER BOOK FOR ALL THE SHEET-METAL TRADES. **$7**⁵⁰

Sheet Metal Workers Handy Book   (AUD-30)

Containing practical information and important facts and figures. Easy to understand. Fundamentals of sheet metal layout work. Clearly written in everyday language. Ready reference index. **$3⁹⁵**

Questions & Answers for Electricians Examinations   (AUD-34)

A practical book to help you prepare for all grades of electricians' license examinations. A helpful review of all the fundamental principles underlying each question and answer needed to prepare you to solve any new or similar problem. Covers the National Electrical Code; questions and answers for license tests; Ohm's law with applied examples; hook-ups for motors; lighting and instruments; A COMPLETE REVIEW FOR ALL ELECTRICAL WORKERS. **$3⁵⁰**

Electrical Power Calculations   (AUD-35)

275 TYPICAL PROBLEMS WORKED OUT. Presents and explains the mathematical formulas and the fundamental electrical laws for all the everday, practical problems in both AC and DC electricity. EVERY ELECTRICAL WORKER AND STUDENT NEEDS THIS MODERN MATHEMATICAL TOOL. **$3⁹⁵**

New Electric Science Dictionary   (AUD-36)

For every worker who has anything to do with electricity. The language of your profession in convenient, alphabetical order so you can instantly locate any word, phrase or term. To be an expert in any line you must talk the language. This new dictionary enables you to understand and explain electrical problems so you can be thoroughly understood. AN ABSOLUTE NECESSITY TO EVERY ELECTRICAL WORKER AND STUDENT. **$3⁵⁰**

Power Plant Engineers Guide   (AUD-37)

A complete steam-engineer's library in one book, with questions and answers. For all Engineers, Firemen, Water Tenders, Oilers, Operators, Repairmen and Applicants for Engineers' License Examinations. 1001 FACTS AND FIGURES AT YOUR FINGER TIPS. **$6⁹⁵**

Questions & Answers for Engineers and Firemans Examinations   (AUD-38)

An aid for stationary, marine, Diesel & hoisting engineers' examinations for all grades **of licenses.** A new concise review explaining in detail the principles, facts and figures of practical engineering. Questions & answers. **$4**

Pumps, Hydraulics, Air Compressors   (AUD-40)

A comprehensive guide for engineers, operators, mechanics, students. Question and answer form. Practical information covering; power & air pumps—condensers—calculations—cooling ponds and towers—water supply—hydraulic rams—dredges—hydraulic drives—machine-tool power—accumulators—elevators—airplane control—presses—turbines—compressor classification—inter and after coolers—regulating devices—installation—lubrication—operation—maintenance—pneumatic hand tools. **$6⁹⁵**

House Heating Guide   (AUD-41)

For heating, ventilating and air-conditioning engineers, plumbers, maintenance men, contractors, building superintendents and mechanics seeking practical, authentic information on heating, ventilating, air conditioning. This comprehensive reference book gives answers to 1001 questions. **$5⁹⁵**

Millwrights & Mechanics Guide   (AUD-42)

Practical information on plant installation, operation, and maintenance. For millwrights, mechanics, erecting maintenance men, riggers, shopmen, servicemen, foremen, inspectors, superintendents. **$6⁹⁵**

Do-It-Yourself Encyclopedia—2 Vols.   (AUD-43)

An all-in-one home repair and project guide for all do-it-yourselfers. Packed with step-by-step plans, thousands of photos, helpful charts. A really authentic, truly monumental, home-repair and home-project guide. **$8⁹⁵**

Water Supply & Sewage Disposal Guide   (AUD-46)

Fully illustrated with detailed data on every phase of rural water-supply, septic-tank, and sewage systems. A MUST BOOK for plumbers, well drillers, home owners and farmers located outside of municipal water and sanitary service areas. **$4**

Gas Engine Manual   (AUD-48)

A completely practical book covering the construction, operation and repair of all types of modern gas engines. Part I covers gas-engine principles; engine parts; auxiliaries; timing methods; ignition systems. Part II covers troubleshooting, adjustment and repairs. **$4**

Outboard Motor & Boating Guide   (AUD-49)

An essential tool for every outboard boating operator. Provides all the information needed to maintain, adjust and repair all types of outboard motors. Gives exploded views of the various parts assemblies, with relative position of each component. **$4**

Encyclopedia of Space Science—4 Vols.   (AUD-50)

The whole marvelous world of space and electronics from A to Z. Four large volumes explain and clarify space and space travel. Completely up-to-date, timely coverage, including thousands of illustrations, many in full color. **$19⁹⁵**

Domestic Compact Auto Repair Manual   (AUD-52)

A practical guide covering all phases of service, maintenance and repair of all popular late-model U.S. compact cars. Includes detailed step-by-step instructions on engine tune-up, fuel and carburetor systems, automatic transmissions, power steering and brakes, and electrical systems. Truly a handy reference manual for mechanics, owners, and service-men. **$5⁹⁵**

Foreign Auto Repair Manual   (AUD-53)

Perfect companion to the Domestic Compact Auto Repair Manual. Contains complete, up-to-date service and repair data for the most popular imported makes, including Fiat, Hillman Minx, M.G., Opel, Peugot, Renault, SAAB, Simca, Volkswagen, and Volvo. Introductory chapters provide complete data on operation and maintenance of fuel and ignition systems. **$5**

Programmed Basic Electricity Course   (AUD-54)

Completely encompasses all facets of electricity fundamentals, including basic series circuits, Ohm's law, parallel circuits, voltage, current, resistance, etc. A unique self-testing study guide for everyone interested in easily learning about electricity and electronics. 10 lessons, 1000 program frames. Perfect for self-study. **$4**

Home Workshop & Tool Handy Book   (AUD-55)

The most modern, up-to-date manual ever designed for home craftsmen and do-it-yourselfers. Tells how to set up your own home workshop (basement, garage, or spare room), all about the various hand and power tools (when, where, and how to use them, etc.). Covers both wood- and metal-working principles and practices. An all-in-one workshop guide for handymen, professionals and students. **$5**

Home Modernizing & Repair Guide   (AUD-56)

FOR THE "DO-IT-YOURSELFER" WHO LIKES TO DO MOST OF HIS HOME UPKEEP JOBS HIMSELF. Here is a practical guide that presents step-by-step instructions, photos, drawings, and other details for many typical home handy-man jobs. Explains what tools are needed, how to use them, and includes tips for doing a really professional job. **$2⁹⁵**

Practical Chemistry for Everyone   (AUD-57)

A practical, easy-to-understand text designed for everyday reference. Comprehensive in scope, here at last is a single volume that covers the subject of chemistry on a level anyone can easily comprehend. Just the thing for those who have never studied chemistry. A useful encyclopedic volume for every home library. **$5⁹⁵**

Auto Engine Tune-Up (AUD-58)

A practical guide to the adjustment of modern autos. Comprehensive and fully illustrated instructions on how to keep your car in top-notch running condition. Covers ignition, valve, cooling, carburetion, and electrical systems on modern auto engines. Includes the use of tune-up test equipment. **$4**95

Gas Appliances and Heating (AUD-59)

A reliable guide to acquaint repairmen and home owners with the construction, operation, and servicing of modern gas-fired appliances such as may be found in the average home. **$3**50

Practical Guide to Mechanics (AUD-61)

A convenient reference book valuable for its practical and concise explanations of the applicable laws of physics. Presents all the basics of mechanics in everyday language, illustrated with practical examples of their applications in various fields. **$4**

Practical Mathematics for Everyone—
2 Vols. (AUD-66)

A concise and reliable guide to the understanding of practical mathematics. People from all walks of life, young and old alike, will find the information contained in these two books just what they have been looking for. The mathematics discussed is for the everyday problems that arise in every household and business.
Vol. 1—Basic Mathematics
Vol. 2—Financial Mathematics $4.95 a volume.   **$8**95

Architects & Builders Guide (AUD-69)

A valuable reference for the architect, builder, and home owner. Explains the effects of natural phenomena such as wind, fire, sound, water, and lightning on all types of buildings. Tells how to minimize their destructive effects and take advantage of their beneficial effects. **$4**

Handbook of Commercial Sound Installations (AUD-92)

A practical complete guide to planning commercial systems, selecting the most suitable equipment, and following through with the most proficient servicing methods. For technicians and the professional and businessman interested in installing a sound system. **$5**95

Practical Guide to Tape Recorders (AUD-93)

Comprehensive guide to tape recorders, covering the history, operation, construction, and maintenance. Service technicians, hobbyists, and even professional recordists can perform their job or pursue their hobby better if they understand the principles of tape recorders. **$4**95

Practical Guide to Auto Radio Repair (AUD-94)

A complete servicing guide for all types of auto radios, including hybrid, all-transistor, and FM . . . PLUS removal instructions for all late-model radios. Fully illustrated. **$4**50

Practical Guide to Citizens Band Radio (AUD-95)

Covers how to select, install, operate, maintain, and adjust all types of CB equipment. Also describes the latest equipment and FCC regulations. For everyone who now uses or plans to use a CB unit, as well as those who install and service such gear. **$4**95

Practical Electronics Projects for the Beginner (AUD-96)

This book can be your first venture in electronics. Clear, concise text plus hundreds of illustrations tell you all you need to know to build numerous functioning projects. HAVE FUN WHILE LEARNING ELECTRONICS FUNDAMENTALS—no previous knowledge necessary. **$4**95

Practical Guide to Servicing Electronic Organs (AUD-97)

Detailed, illustrated discussions of the operation and servicing of electronic organs. Including models by Allen, Baldwin, Conn, Hammond, Kinsman, Lowrey, Magnavox, Thomas, and Wurlitzer. **$4**95

Carpentry and Building   (AUD-98)

Answers to the problems encountered in today's building trades. The actual questions asked of an architect by carpenters and builders are answered in this book. No apprentice or journeyman carpenter should be without the help this book can offer. **$4⁹⁵**

Practical Guide to Building Maintenance   (AUD-99)

A comprehensive book on the practical aspects of building maintenance. Chapters are included on: painting and decorating; plumbing and pipe fitting; carpentry; calking and glazing; concrete and masonry; roofing; sheet metal; electrical; air conditioning and refrigeration; insect and rodent control; heating; maintenance management; custodial practices: A MUST BOOK FOR BUILDING OWNERS, MANAGERS, AND MAINTENANCE PERSONNEL. **$4⁹⁵**

Practical Guide to Fluid Power   (AUD-100)

An essential book for the owner, operator, supervisor, or maintenance man concerned with hydraulic or pneumatic equipment. A complete coverage of modern design, application, and repair of fluid power devices. Fully illustrated. **$6⁹⁵**

Practical Science Projects in Electricity/Electronics   (AUD-102)

An ideal collection of projects in electricity and electronics for the beginner. Practical projects constructed on pegboard with simple easily obtained parts make basic electronic principles fun to learn. Young and old alike will find this book the answer to their search for knowledge. **$4⁹⁵**

TO ORDER AUDEL BOOKS mail this handy form to
Theo. Audel & Co., 4300 W. 62nd
Indianapolis, Indiana 46206

Please send me for FREE EXAMINATION books marked (x) below. If I decide to keep them I agree to mail $3 in 7 days on each book or set ordered and further mail $3 monthly on each book or set until I have paid price plus shipping charges. Otherwise, I will return them.

☐ (AUD-25) Answers on Blueprint Reading.......$ 4.95
☐ (AUD-69) Architects and Builders Guide....... 4.00
☐ (AUD-58) Auto Engine Tune-Up................ 4.95
☐ (AUD- 1) Automobile Guide.................. 6.95
☐ (AUD- 8) Carpenters & Builders Guides (4 Vols.) 16.95
    ☐_____Single volumes sold separately..ea. 4.95
☐ (AUD-98) Carpentry and Building............. 4.95
☐ (AUD-14B) Commercial Refrigeration.......... 5.95
☐ (AUD- 9) Diesel Engine Manual.............. 6.00
☐ (AUD-43) Do-It-Yourself Encyclopedia (2 Vols.).. 8.95
☐ (AUD-52) Domestic Compact Auto Repair Manual 5.95
☐ (AUD-35) Electrical Power Calculations........ 3.95
☐ (AUD-27) Electric Motors................... 5.95
☐ (AUD-50) Encyclopedia of Space Science (4 Vols.) 19.95
☐ (AUD-53) Foreign Auto Repair Manual......... 5.00
☐ (AUD-59) Gas Appliances and Heating......... 4.25
☐ (AUD-48) Gas Engine Manual................. 4.00
☐ (AUD-92) Handbook of Commercial Sound
    Installations 5.95
☐ (AUD- 4) Handy Book of Practical Electricity.. 5.95
☐ (AUD- 2) Home Appliance Servicing........... 6.95
☐ (AUD-56) Home Modernizing & Repair Guide... 2.95
☐ (AUD-14A) Home Refrigeration and Air
    Conditioning 6.95
☐ (AUD-55) Home Workshop & Tool Handy Book... 5.00
☐ (AUD-41) House Heating Guide.............. 5.95
☐ (AUD-12) Machinist Library (3 Vols.).......... 13.50
    ☐_____Single volumes sold separately..ea. 4.95
☐ (AUD-26) Masons & Builders Guides (4 Vols.).. 10.50
    ☐_____Single volumes sold separately..ea. 3.00
☐ (AUD-11) Mathematics & Calculations for
    Mechanics 4.95
☐ (AUD-42) Millwrights & Mechanics Guide...... 6.95
☐ (AUD-15A) New Electric Library (10 Vols.)..... 25.00
    ☐_____Single volumes sold separately..ea. 3.00
☐ (AUD-36) New Electric Science Dictionary..... 3.50
☐ (AUD-28) Oil Burner Guide................. 3.95

☐ (AUD-49) Outboard Motor & Boating Guide.... 4.00
☐ (AUD- 7) Painting & Decorating Manual....... 4.95
☐ (AUD- 6) Plumbers & Pipe Fitters Library (3 Vols.) 9.95
    ☐_____Single volumes sold separately..ea. 3.50
☐ (AUD-37) Power Plant Engineers Guide........ 6.95
☐ (AUD-57) Practical Chemistry for Everyone.... 5.95
☐ (AUD-96) Practical Electronics Projects
    for the Beginner......................... 4.95
☐ (AUD-94) Practical Guide to Auto Radio Repair.. 4.50
☐ (AUD-99) Practical Guide to Building
    Maintenance 4.95
☐ (AUD-95) Practical Guide to Citizens Band Radio. 4.95
☐ (AUD-100) Practical Guide to Fluid Power...... 6.95
☐ (AUD-61) Practical Guide to Mechanics....... 4.00
☐ (AUD-97) Practical Guide to Servicing
    Electronic Organs 4.95
☐ (AUD-93) Practical Guide to Tape Recorders.... 4.95
☐ (AUD-66) Practical Mathematics for Everyone
    (2 Vols.) 8.95
    ☐_____Single volumes sold separately..ea. 4.95
☐ (AUD-102) Practical Science Projects in
    Electricity/Electronics 4.95
☐ (AUD-54) Programmed Basic Electricity Course. 4.00
☐ (AUD-40) Pumps, Hydraulics, Air Compressors.. 6.95
☐ (AUD-34) Questions & Answers for Electricians
    Examinations 3.95
☐ (AUD-38) Questions & Answers for Engineers &
    Firemans Examinations 4.00
☐ (AUD-3A) Radiomans Guide 5.00
☐ (AUD-29) Sheet Metal Pattern Layouts........ 7.50
☐ (AUD-30) Sheet Metal Workers Handy Book ... 3.95
☐ (AUD-3B) Television Service Manual........... 5.00
☐ (AUD- 5) Truck & Tractor Guide............. 5.95
☐ (AUD-46) Water Supply & Sewage
    Disposal Guide 4.00
☐ (AUD-10) Welders Guide 4.95
☐ (AUD-13) Wiring Diagrams for Light & Power... 4.00

Name_____

Address_____

City_____State_____Zip_____

Occupation_____Employed by_____

☐ **SAVE SHIPPING CHARGES! Enclose Full Payment
With Coupon and We Pay Shipping Charges.** PRINTED IN USA